Classic Songs of Am

Arrangements for Piano, Guitar and Electronic Keyboard
by Dan Fox

Illustrations from the Museum of American Folk Art

A Donna Martin Book

Andrews and McMeel · *A Universal Press Syndicate Company* · Kansas City

Contents

Quiltmaker unknown
Bird of Paradise Quilt Top (detail)
Vicinity of Albany, New York; 1858–1863
Appliquéd cotton; wool;
silk including velvet on muslin;
silk embroidery including silk
chenille thread, ink.
$84^{1}/_{2}$ x $69^{5}/_{8}$ in. (214.6 x 176.9 cm)
Gift of the Trustees of the Museum of
American Folk Art
1979.7.1

S. Fagley (dates unknown)
Bald Eagle and Arrows; United States; 1872
Pen and ink on paper; $9^3/_4$ x 11 in. (24.8 x 27.9 cm)
Gift of Dr. Lillian Malcove
1977.17.1

Battle Hymn of the Republic

Words by Julia Ward Howe

Music: Anonymous

THE EARLIEST KNOWN PUBLICATION of this great marching song is 1859, when it was known as "Say, Brothers, Will You Meet Us." The same tune with a new set of words became very popular in the North as "John Brown's Body" soon after the outbreak of the Civil War in the spring of 1861. Julia Ward Howe (1819–1910), a well-known reformer and writer on social issues, heard federal troops singing that tune with the words "John Brown's body lies a-moldering in the grave . . ." in November of 1861. With that melody in mind, she wrote a new set of words, the ones we sing today, as "The Battle Hymn of the Republic," and published them in April of 1862. Although many people have been suggested as the composer of the music, no one knows his identity for sure.

Like a slow march

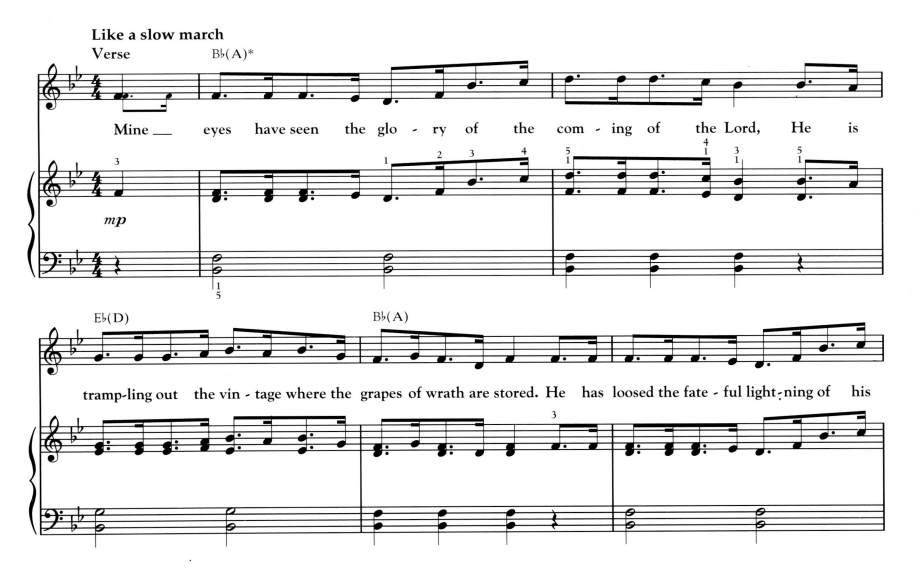

*Chords in parentheses are for guitar with capo across 1st fret.

2. I have seen Him in the watchfires of a hundred circling camps;
They have builded Him an altar in the evening dews and damps;
I can read His righteous sentence by the dim and flaring lamps;
His day is marching on.
(repeat chorus)

3. He has sounded forth the trumpet that shall never call retreat;
He is sifting out the hearts of men before His judgment seat;
Oh, be swift, my soul, to answer Him, be jubilant, my feet!
Our God is marching on.
(repeat chorus)

Artist unknown
Standing Sentinel Whirligig, United States
Late 19th century
Wood, paint, metal, glass eyes; $40^1/_4$ x 5 in.
(103.5 x 12.7 cm) with base
Bequest of Richard Bruce E. LaCont
1989.24.1

Artist unknown
Miniature Pin: Soldiers; United States; 1830–1840
Watercolor on ivory; $1^1/_4$ x 1 in. (3.2 x 2.5 cm)
Joseph Martinson Memorial Fund,
Frances and Paul Martinson
1981.12.29

America the Beautiful

Words by Katharine Lee Bates

Music by Samuel Augustus Ward

KATHARINE LEE BATES (1859-1929) wrote the beloved words to this song in 1895 after a climb up Pike's Peak in Colorado. There the view inspired her to convey the beauty and majesty of America. Although many composers vied for the honor of setting Bates's words to music, she herself chose the melody "Materna," which Samuel Augustus Ward (1847-1903) had composed in 1882 for his hymn "O Mother Dear, Jerusalem."

Broadly, but without dragging

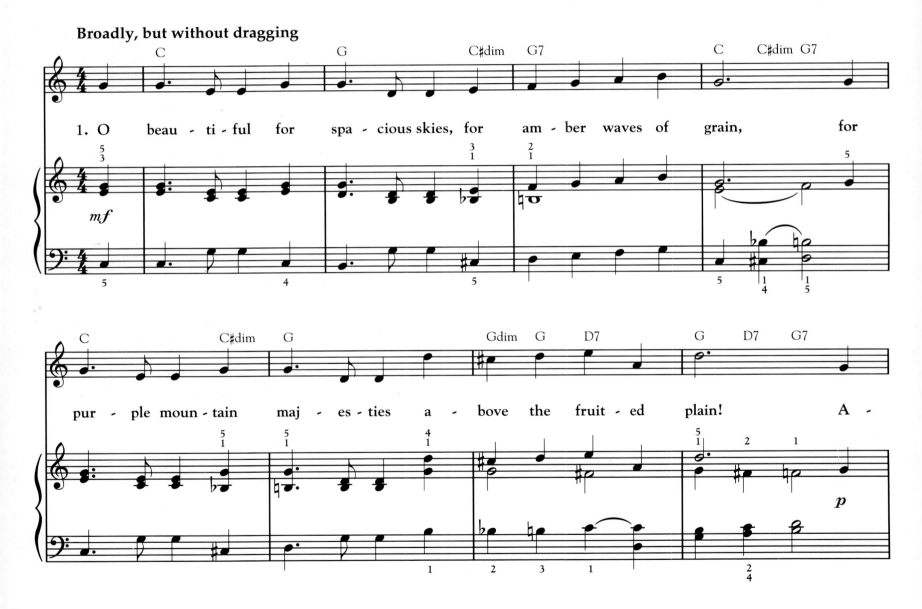

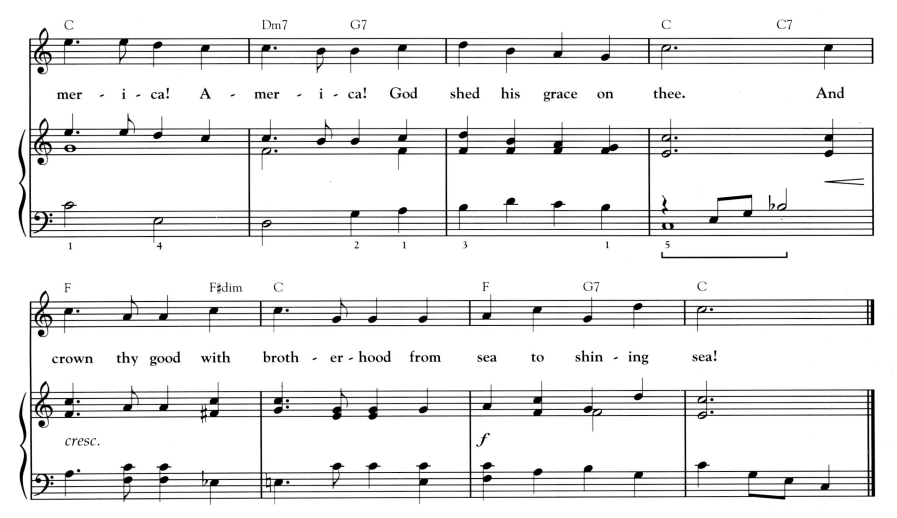

mer - i - ca! A - mer - i - ca! God shed his grace on thee. And

crown thy good with broth - er - hood from sea to shin - ing sea!

cresc.

f

2. O beautiful for pilgrim feet,
   Whose stern, impassioned stress
   A thoroughfare for freedom beat
   Across the wilderness!
   America! America!
   God mend thine every flaw.
   Confirm thy soul in self-control,
   Thy liberty in law.

3. O beautiful for heroes proved
   In liberating strife,
   Who more than self their country loved,
   And mercy more than life!
   America! America!
   May God thy gold refine,
   Till all success be nobleness,
   And every gain divine.

4. O beautiful for patriot dream
   That sees beyond the years
   Thine alabaster cities gleam
   Undimmed by human tears!
   America! America!
   God shed his grace on thee,
   And crown thy good with brotherhood
   From sea to shining sea.

Possibly Mary Simon b. 1810
Baltimore-Style Album Quilt Top (detail)
Probably Baltimore, Maryland; 1849–1852
Hand-sewn, appliquéd cotton, ink
109 x 105 in. (276.9 x 266.7 cm)
Gift of Mr. and Mrs. James O. Keene
1984.41.1

The Star-Spangled Banner

Words by Francis Scott Key

Music probably by John Stafford Smith

MOST AMERICANS ARE FAMILIAR with the story of Francis Scott Key's writing the words to our national anthem while witnessing the British bombardment of Fort McHenry in Baltimore harbor during the War of 1812. Less well known is the fact that many writers had composed different words to the same melody. In fact, Key himself had used the melody in an 1805 tribute to Stephen Decatur, the hero of the war against the Tripoli pirates, called "When the Warrior Returns."

The melody, originally titled "To Anacreon in Heaven," was written in England in about 1750 and is attributed to John Stafford Smith, a member of a club called the Anacreontic Society. It was used as a drinking song! If you sing the first six notes you can almost see the bibulous crowd raising their glasses on high. "The Star-Spangled Banner" didn't become our national anthem until 1931.

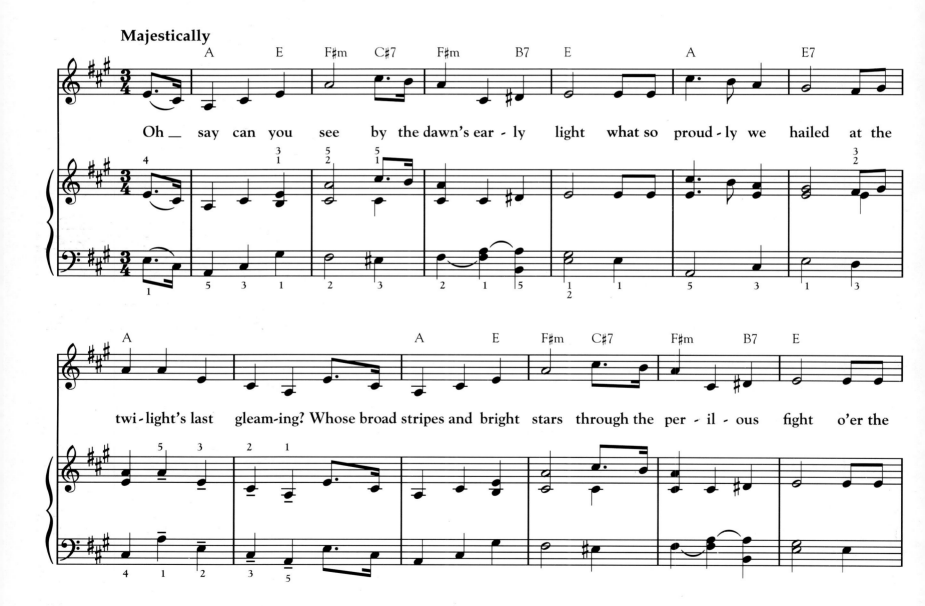

When Johnny Comes Marching Home

Words by Louis Lambert

Music: Traditional

LOUIS LAMBERT WAS THE PSEUDONYM of bandleader Patrick Gilmore. Gilmore's Band was highly popular around the time of the Civil War, not least because Gilmore was a master showman who used real cannons, anvils, and other sound effects at his concerts. Although he is definitely the author of the words, the origins of the melody are uncertain. Gilmore himself described it as "a Negro tune," but the melody has a distinct Irish flavor. Since Gilmore was born in Ireland, it seems likely that wherever the tune comes from, he put his own stamp on it.

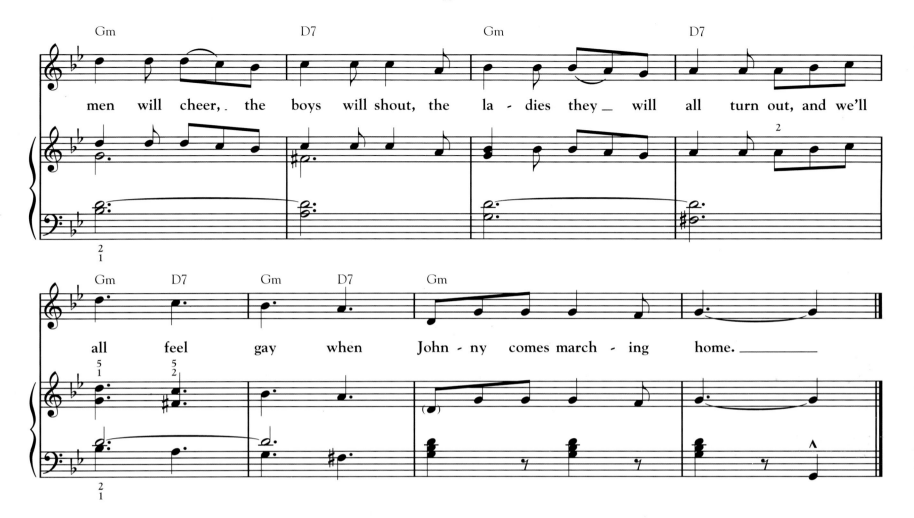

men will cheer, the boys will shout, the la - dies they will all turn out, and we'll all feel gay when John - ny comes march - ing home.

2. The old church bell will peal with joy,
   Hurrah, hurrah!
   To welcome home our darling boy,
   Hurrah, hurrah!
   The village lads and lassies say,
   With roses they will strew the way,
   And we'll all feel gay when
   Johnny comes marching home.

3. Get ready for the Jubilee,
   Hurrah, hurrah!
   We'll give the hero three times three,
   Hurrah, hurrah!
   The laurel wreath is ready now
   To place upon his loyal brow,
   And we'll all feel gay when
   Johnny comes marching home.

Artist unknown
Flag Gate (detail); Jefferson County,
New York; c. 1876
Polychromed wood, iron, brass
$39^{1}/_{2}$ x 57 x $3^{3}/_{4}$ in.
(100.3 x 144.8 x 9.5 cm)
Gift of Herbert Waide Hemphill, Jr.
1962.1.1

Yankee Doodle

Words attributed to Dr. Shuckburgh   *Music: Traditional*

SUPPOSEDLY, A CERTAIN DR. SHUCKBURGH came upon an assembly of Continental troops during the French and Indian War (1754–63) and was so amused at their rag-tag look that he wrote these words to an old Irish folk tune, "All the Way to Galway." The words tell us that the song was written before the Revolution because George Washington is still only a captain. "Hasty pudding" was a type of mush made from cornmeal. The word "Yankee" comes from the Dutch "Jahnke" or Johnny. A "doodle" was a foolish person or simpleton. "Macaroni" referred not to the pasta we eat today, but to fancy or foppish clothes. So what the song really is saying is "Look at Johnny Simpleton. He sticks a feather in his cap and thinks that makes him a dandy." But the Continentals had the last laugh when "Yankee Doodle" was played at the British surrender at Yorktown.

With spirit

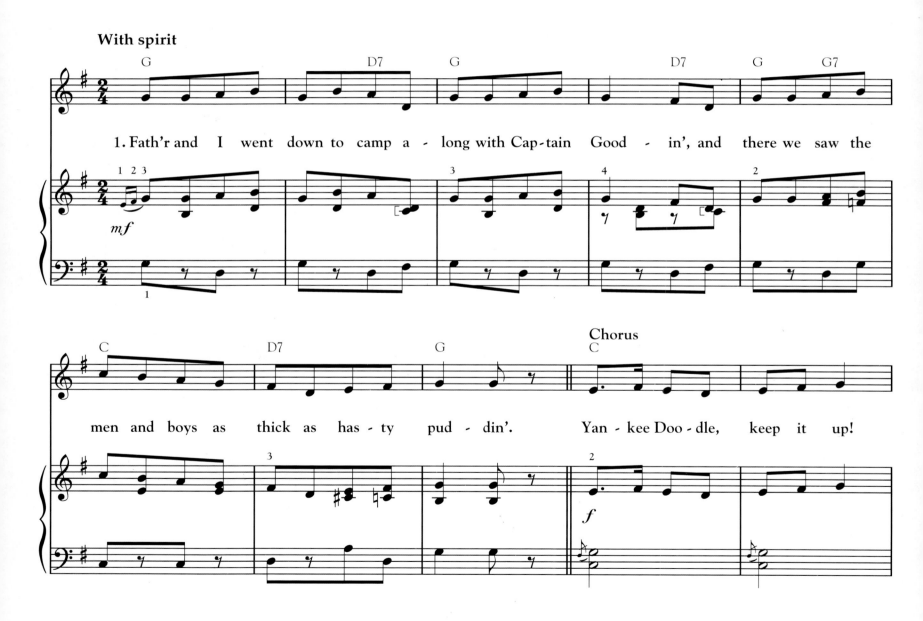

1. Fath'r and I went down to camp a - long with Cap-tain Good - in', and there we saw the

men and boys as thick as has - ty pud - din'. Yan - kee Doo - dle, keep it up!

Yan-kee Doo-dle dan - dy. Mind the mu - sic and the step, and with the girls be hand - y.

2. And there we see a thousand men, as rich as Squire David,
   And what they wasted ev'ry day, I wish it could be savèd.
   (repeat chorus)

3. And there was Captain Washington upon a strapping stallion,
   A-giving orders to his men; I guess there was a million.
   (chorus)

4. And then the feathers on his hat, they looked so very fine, ah!
   I wanted peskily to get to give to my Jemima.
   (chorus)

5. Yankee Doodle went to London just to ride a pony,
   Stuck a feather in his cap and called it macaroni.
   (chorus)

Attributed to Henry Young (1792–1861)
General George Washington on Horseback
Lycoming County, Pennsylvania; 1825–1835.
Pen and ink, pencil, and watercolor on wove paper
$13^5/_8$ x $9^3/_4$ in. (34.6 x 24.8 cm)
Gift of Ralph O. Esmerian
1993.10.1

Dixie

(I Wish I Was in Dixie's Land)

Words and Music by Dan D. Emmett

THIS UNOFFICIAL NATIONAL ANTHEM OF THE SOUTH was written by a northerner—and a staunch supporter of the Union and Abraham Lincoln at that. In 1859, Dan Emmett was a well-known minstrel-show entertainer when he was asked to create a musical number, called a "walk-around," to serve as a big finish to the show he was in. The song was an immediate success and was soon printed all over the South in illegal, or "pirated," editions. By the time the Civil War ended in 1865, Emmett had lost any possibility of protecting his copyright

and had to be content with seeing it become one of America's best loved songs in both the North and the South.

The name "Dixie" comes from a special ten-dollar bill printed in New Orleans in the early 1800s. New Orleans was a French-speaking city, so the government printed the word *dix*, which is ten in French, on the bills. Because Americans did not realize that the word was pronounced "deece," the money became known as "dixies," and the name eventually came to signify the South itself.

*Chord symbols in parentheses are for guitar with capo across 1st fret.

way down south in Dix - ie! A - way, a - way, a - way down south in Dix - ie!

Possibly Mary Simon b. 1810
Baltimore-Style Album Quilt Top (details)
Probably Baltimore, Maryland; 1849–1852
Hand-sewn, appliquéd cotton, ink
109 x 105 in. (276.9 x 266.7 cm)
Gift of Mr. and Mrs. James O. Keene
1984.41.1

A Hot Time in the Old Town

(THERE'LL BE A HOT TIME IN THE OLD TOWN TONIGHT)

Words by Joe Hayden *Music by Theodore A. Metz*

WRITTEN IN 1896 by a couple of song-and-dance men, the original title was "A Hot Time in Old Town." Old Town was a tiny hamlet in Louisiana, and the song comments ironically on the lack of action there. A few years later, it became the unofficial marching song of the troops in the Spanish-American War in 1898. In the mid-1920s it was recorded in a sultry jazz arrangement by that greatest of early blues singers, Bessie Smith.

Over There

Words and Music by George M. Cohan

THE FAMOUS IRISH-AMERICAN SHOWMAN and songwriter George M. Cohan won a Congressional Medal of Honor for this song, written at the time the United States entered World War I. The simple melody is based on a bugle call, and as songwriter Oscar Hammerstein once commented about the words, "It is Cohan's genius to say what everybody else is subconsciously feeling." The song went on to inspire the doughboys in the first war and the G.I.'s in the second.

Just about everybody knew the words to "Over There," except for Cohan himself, who once forgot them at a benefit performance. His friends Irving Berlin and Joe Laurie Jr. had to jump on stage to help him finish the song. Cohan's statue stands in Times Square overlooking his beloved Broadway.

Brightly, like a march

When You Were Sweet Sixteen

Words and music by James Thornton

WHEN JAMES THORNTON'S WIFE ASKED HIM if he still loved her, Thornton, like many husbands before and after, came up with a soothing answer: "I love you like I did when you were sweet sixteen." Unlike other husbands, however, Thornton put it to music, published it, and sold more than a million copies of sheet music. The song is still a favorite at singalongs and other convivial occasions.

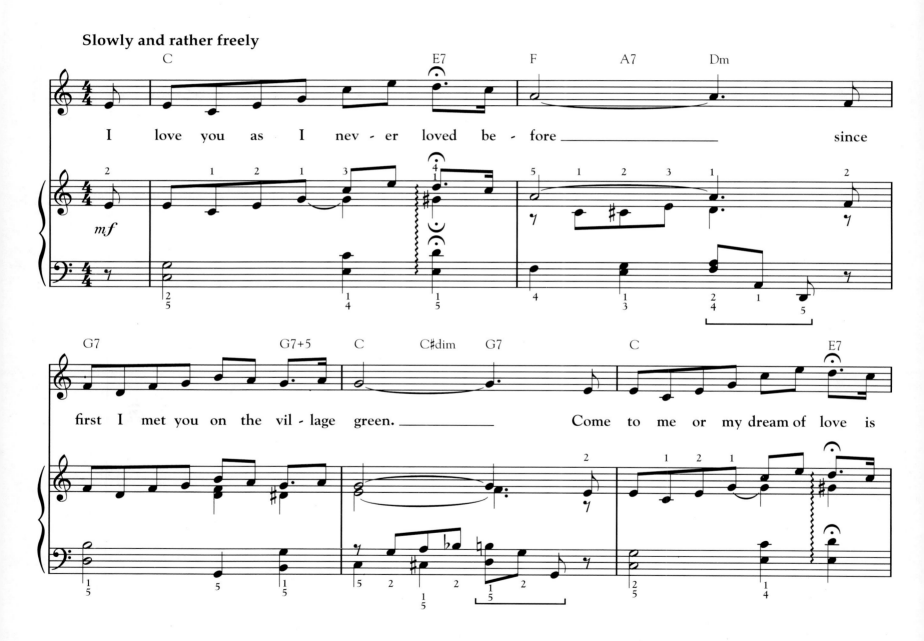

o'er; _____ I love you as I loved you when you were sweet, when you were sweet six-teen.

Ruthy Rogers (dates unknown)
Sampler; Marblehead, Massachusetts; c. 1789
Silk on linen; $10^{1}/_{2}$ x 9 in. (26.7 x 22.9 cm)
Collection of Ralph Esmerian

Sweet Adeline

(YOU'RE THE FLOWER OF MY HEART)

Words by Richard H. Gerard

Music by Harry Armstrong

THIS PERENNIAL BARBERSHOP FAVORITE was originally titled "My Old New England Home" when composed in 1896. A few years later it became "Sweet Rosalie." Then, in 1903, in honor of the world-famous diva Adelina Patti, it got its ultimate name, and with it, tremendous success. Three years later the song became the official campaign song of Boston mayoral candidate John F. "Honey" Fitzgerald, grandfather of the 35th president of the United States, John Fitzgerald Kennedy.

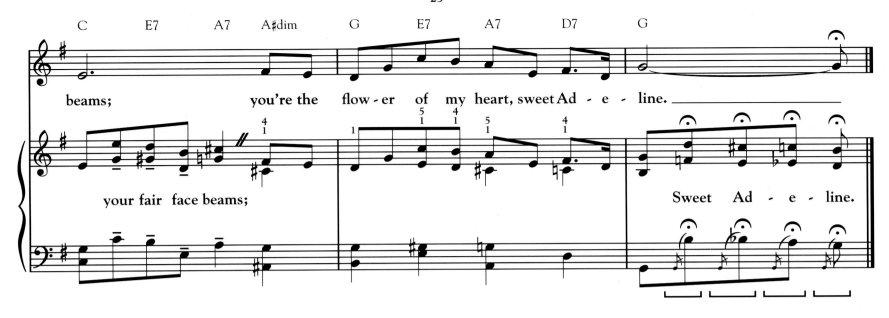

beams; you're the flow - er of my heart, sweet Ad - e - line. _____

your fair face beams; Sweet Ad - e - line.

Hannah Carter (dates unknown)
Lady with a Fan, Boston, Massachusetts; c. 1750
Crewel yarn on fine canvas, 17 3/4 x 16 in.
(45.1 x 40.6 cm)
Collection of Ralph Esmerian

There's a Long Long Trail A-Winding

Words by Stoddard King   *Music by Zo Elliot*

THE WRITERS WERE JUST SENIORS at Yale when they penned this nostalgic ballad in 1913. Every American publisher they submitted it to turned it down. Finally Elliot had it published in England, and when war broke out in 1914 the song became a hit. Although the song is indelibly associated with World War I,

King actually had been reading about Napoleon's retreat from Moscow just before jotting down the words. The opening measures may sound a little familiar; that's because they are identical to the first few bars of James Bland's earlier "In the Evening by the Moonlight."

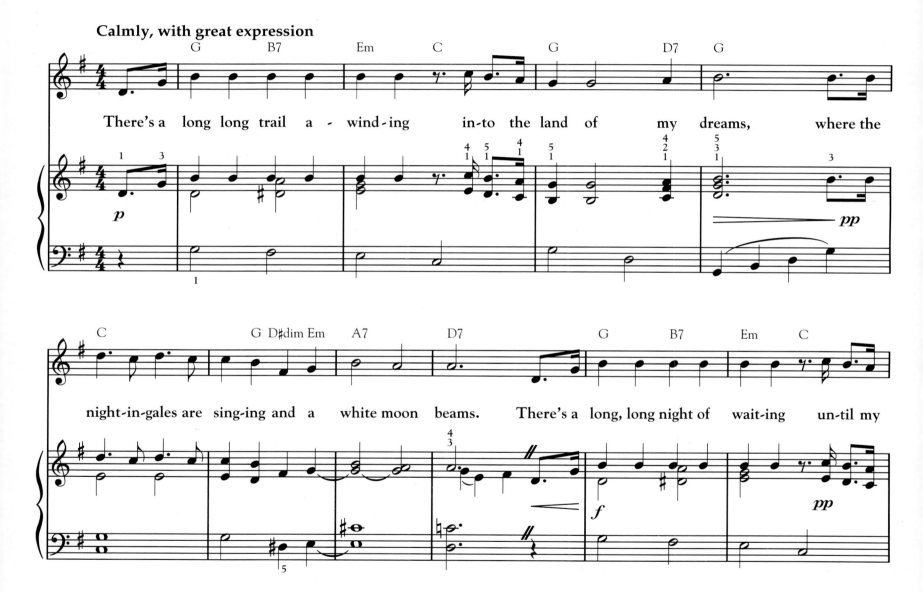

Calmly, with great expression

There's a long long trail a - wind-ing in-to the land of my dreams, where the

night-in-gales are sing-ing and a white moon beams. There's a long, long night of wait-ing un-til my

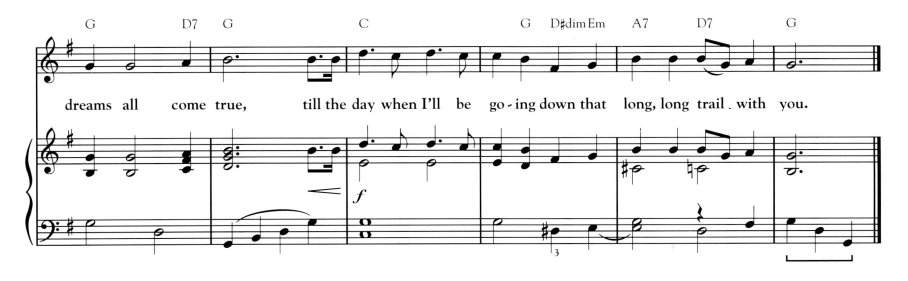

dreams all come true, till the day when I'll be go-ing down that long, long trail with you.

Artist unknown
Romantic Landscape; vicinity of Sturbridge,
Massachusetts; 1830–1850
Watercolor on paper; 15 7/8 x 20 in.
(40.3 x 50.8 cm)
Gift of Cyril Irwin Nelson
in memory of his grandparents,
Guerdon Stearns and Elinor Irwin Holden,
and in honor of his parents, Cyril Arthur
and Elise Macy Nelson
1983.29.3

Down by the Old Mill Stream

Words and Music by Tell Taylor

ONE OF THE BEST-LOVED BARBERSHOP BALLADS, this gem sold over two million copies of sheet music in 1910. To this day it's a favorite of harmony singers everywhere. And although its composer, Tell Taylor, continued to work as a songwriter all his life, he never had another hit.

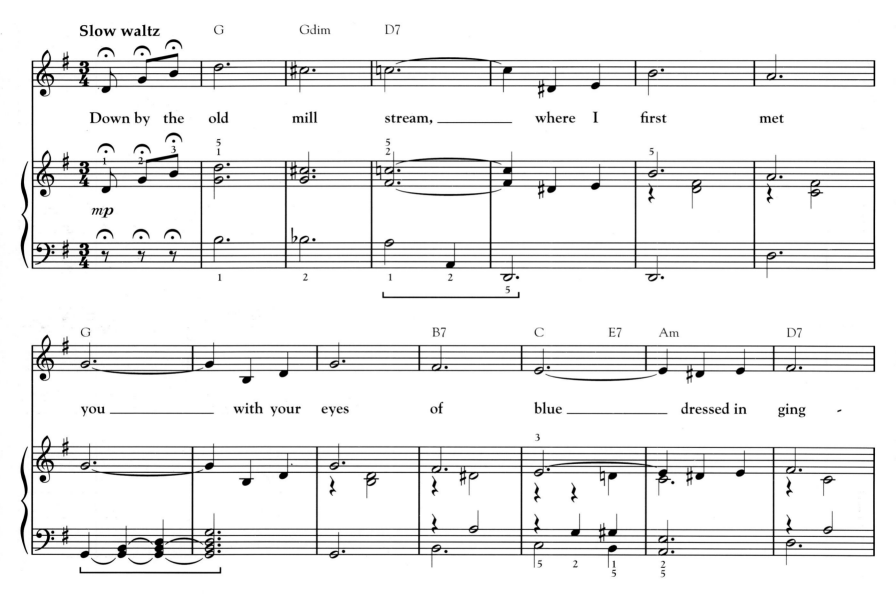

Down by the old mill stream, _____ where I first met

you _____ with your eyes of blue _____ dressed in ging -

Will You Love Me in December As You Do in May?

Words by James J. Walker

Music by Ernest R. Ball

ERNEST R. BALL HAD HIS FIRST of many hits with this song. Later he wrote such fine standards as "Let the Rest of the World Go By," "A Little Bit of Heaven," and "When Irish Eyes Are Smiling." Lyric writer Jimmy Walker had an entirely different career. The royalties from this ballad paid his way through law school, and from there he entered politics. He was elected mayor of New York City in 1926, but was forced from office by scandals in his administration and went into self-imposed exile in Europe. This was his theme song. It was played when he ran for mayor, while he was in office, when he returned from exile in 1935, and finally at his funeral in 1946. New Yorkers remember Jimmy Walker fondly. Perhaps he wasn't the best the city ever had, but while he was mayor New York seemed to be the most interesting and exciting place in the world.

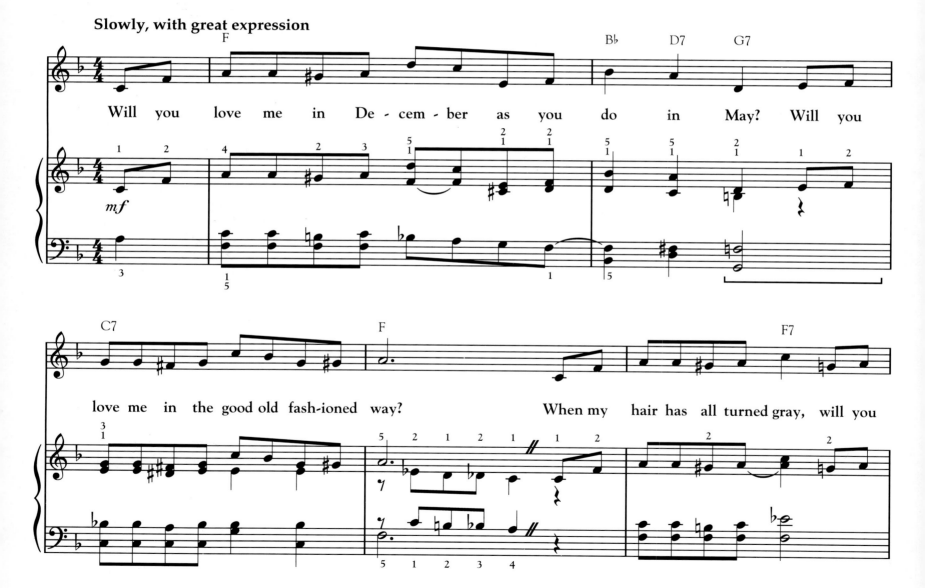

kiss me then and say that you love me in De - cem - ber as you do in May?

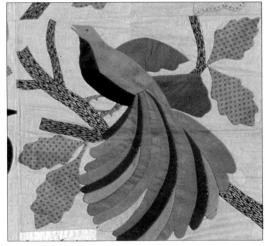

Quiltmaker unknown
Bird of Paradise Quilt Top (details)
Vicinity of Albany, New York; 1858–1863
Appliquéd cotton; wool;
silk including velvet on muslin;
silk embroidery including silk
chenille thread, ink
$84^1/_2$ x $69^5/_8$ in. (214.6 x 176.9 cm)
Gift of the Trustees of the Museum of
American Folk Art
1979.7.1

You Tell Me Your Dream

(I'LL TELL YOU MINE)

Words by Seymour Rice and A. H. Brown

Music by Charles N. Daniels

THIS 1908 BALLAD WAS TYPICAL of the sentimental tunes popular before World War I. Singing groups love it because of its juicy barbershop chords.

Also, by putting the melody in 4/4 time, jazz musicians created a Dixieland standard.

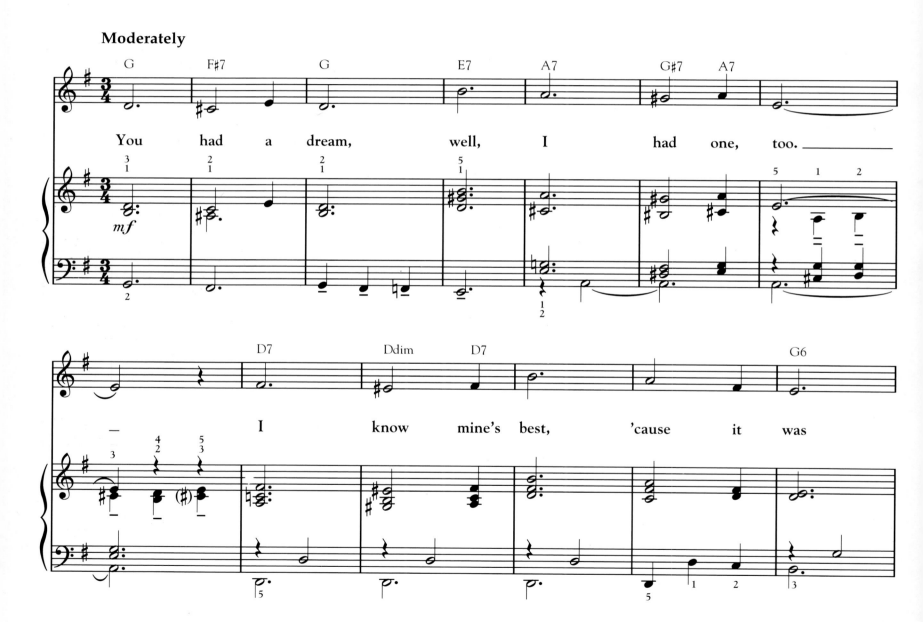

The House of the Rising Sun

Traditional

This tells the story of poor country girls who look for excitement in big cities like New Orleans. All too often they find only poverty, shame, and degradation. The melody is related to "Lord Barnard and Lady Musgrave," an old English ballad that dates back at least 300 years. In 1964 an English rock group, The Animals, had a hit with an updated version of the song.

Moderately slow

1. There is a house in New Or-leans they call "The Ris - ing Sun."

It's been the ruin of man-y a poor girl, and I, oh Lord, am one.

2. My father was a trav'ling man,
   Left my mother when I was one.
   Kept drinkin' and a-gamblin'
   Until his time was done.

3. Go tell my baby sister, say
   "Don't do as I have done.
   And keep away from gambling men
   And the house called 'The Rising Sun.'"

4. I'm headed home to Arkansas,
   My race is almost run.
   I'll say farewell to New Orleans
   And "The House of the Rising Sun."

Probably Rebecca Scattergood Savery (1770–1855)
Sunburst Quilt; Philadelphia, Pennsylvania; 1835–1845
Hand-pieced, hand-quilted roller-printed cottons,
118^1/$_2$ x 125^1/$_8$ in. (301 x 317.8 cm)
Gift of Marie D. and Charles A. T. O'Neill
1979.26.2

Some of These Days

Words and Music by Shelton Brooks

AFRICAN-AMERICAN SONGWRITER Shelton Brooks came up with this song in 1910. Thanks to electrifying performances by white vaudeville star Sophie Tucker (who adopted it as her theme song) the song became very popular, sold many copies of sheet music, and was recorded by virtually all the great performers of the 1920s, '30s, and '40s. Unfortunately for Brooks, he had sold all the rights for the pitiful sum of thirty dollars. He learned his lesson, however, and

his next hit, "The Darktown Strutter's Ball" (1917) made him a rich man.

Incidentally, this latter song was the first jazz record ever made. It was recorded by the Original Dixieland Jass Band in 1917. (Yes, *Jass!* Executives at the Victor Company thought that "jazz" was too naughty a word to use on a record label!)

Just a Closer Walk with Thee

Traditional

THIS SPIRITUAL ORIGINATED in nineteenth-century black America, but it has also been a favorite of country and jazz musicians. Red Foley had a country hit with it in 1950, and Dixieland bands find it one of their most requested numbers. The last line was the inspiration for the Beatles' song "Let It Be."

Moderately, with a steady beat

*Chord symbols in parentheses are for guitar with capo across 3rd fret.

walk-ing close with thee, _____ let it be, dear Lord, let it be. _____

2. I am weak but thou art strong;
   Jesus, keep me from all wrong;
   I'll be satisfied as long,
   As I walk, dear Lord, close to thee.

3. Through this world of toil and snares,
   If I falter, Lord, who cares?
   Who with me my burden shares?
   None but thee, dear Lord, none but thee.

4. When my feeble life is o'er,
   Time for me will be no more;
   Guide me gently, safely on,
   To thy shore, dear Lord, to thy shore.

Susan Arrowood (dates unknown)
Sacret Bibel Quilt; West Chester,
Pennsylvania; 1875–1895
Appliquéd and embroidered cotton, including lace; silk
including velvet; wool, ink with cotton embroidery
88 1/2 x 72 in. (224.8 x 182.9 cm)
Gift of the Amicus Foundation, Inc.
and Evelyn and Leonard Lauder
1986.20.1

Bill Bailey

(WON'T YOU PLEASE COME HOME?)

Words and Music by Hughie Cannon

THIS PERENNIAL FAVORITE was written toward the beginning of the ragtime era (about 1895–1920), by vaudevillian Hughie Cannon. The song seems to have been inspired by the marital difficulties of Cannon's friend, one Willard

Godfrey Bailey, who was a trombonist and music teacher in Jackson, Michigan, where Cannon wrote this in 1902.

Moderately, with a beat

Lonesome Road

Traditional

THIS AFRICAN-AMERICAN SPIRITUAL was the basis for a popular song used in the first movie version of *Showboat*. It has had many recordings, the best being Louis (Satchmo) Armstrong's, sung and played as only he could.

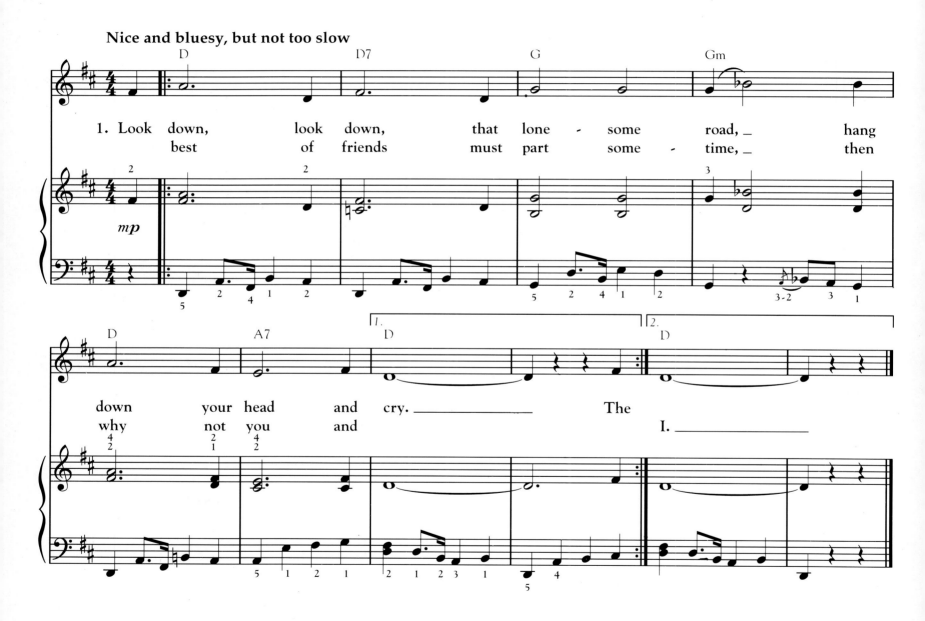

2. Look down, look down that lonesome road,
   Before you travel on;
   Look up, look up and greet your maker,
   'Fore Gabriel blows his horn.

3. Look down, look down, it's weary walkin',
   Trudgin' down that lonesome road.
   Look up, look up and greet your maker,
   'Fore Gabriel blows his horn.

4. (Repeat 1st verse)

Artist unknown
Archangel Gabriel Weathervane
United States; c. 1840
Painted sheet metal; 35 x 32^1/$_2$ x 1^1/$_4$ in.
(88.9 x 82.6 x 3.2 cm)
Gift of Mrs. Adele Earnest
1963.1.1

Alexander's Ragtime Band

Words and Music by Irving Berlin

IN 1911, A YOUNG IRVING BERLIN was asked to write a song for an upcoming Friar's Club evening. No one could have predicted that this song would become one of the great American popular standards. Berlin wedded a jaunty lyric with a catchy marchlike melody that quotes a bugle call and Stephen Foster's "Old Folks at Home." This song went on to sell millions of copies of sheet music and in 1938 became the title of an all-Berlin musical motion picture. Songwriter Jerome Kern was once asked what Berlin's place was in American music. "Berlin has no *place* in American music," Kern replied. "He *is* American music!"

Git Along, Little Dogies

Traditional

Thanks to innumerable pulp novels and Hollywood movies, cowboys of the Old West became larger-than-life figures, riding the range and righting wrongs. As this song tells us, the reality was far less romantic. The cowboy's life was tedious, uncomfortable, and dangerous. It paid very little and required a cowboy's twenty-four-hour-a-day commitment to his charges.

A dogie is a little calf that has lost its mother. Because it can't drink mother's milk, the calf eats grass which causes its belly to swell up. Cowboys called them "dough guts," which over the years became "dogies."

Loping along

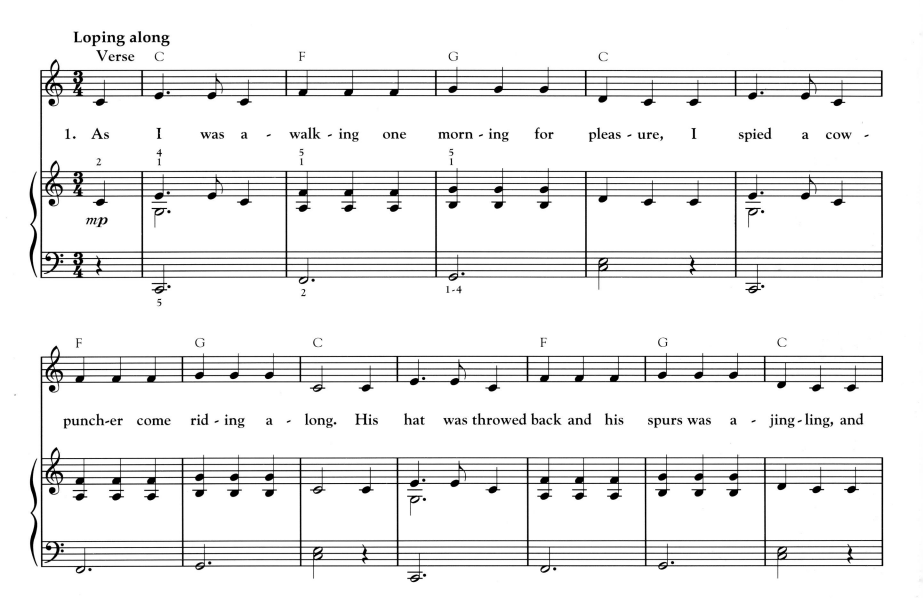

1. As I was a-walk-ing one morn-ing for pleas-ure, I spied a cow-punch-er come rid-ing a-long. His hat was throwed back and his spurs was a-jing-ling, and

2. It's early in spring that we round up the dogies,
   And mark 'em and brand 'em and bob off their tails;
   We round up our horses and load the chuck wagon,
   And then throw the dogies out onto the trail.
   (repeat chorus)

3. It's whoopin' and yellin' and a-drivin' them dogies,
   Oh, how I wish that you would go on;
   It's a-whoopin' and punchin' and go on-a, little dogies,
   For you know, Wyoming is to be your new home.
   (repeat chorus)

4. Some cowboys go up the trail just for pleasure,
   But that's where they get it most awfully wrong,
   For nobody knows what trouble they give us,
   As we go driving them all along.
   (repeat chorus)

Elijah Pierce (1892–1984)
Seeking Gold in the West; Columbus, Ohio; c. 1950
Carved and polychromed wood
12 x 24$\frac{1}{2}$ in. (30.5 x 62.2 cm)
Gift of Mr. and Mrs. Charles Prendergast
1972.2.1

The Drunken Sailor

Traditional

THE MEN WHO WORKED ON SAILING SHIPS had to be fearless and strong, and had to have incredible endurance. To make their work go easier, they made up songs called *chanteys* that they could sing while performing tasks together.

"The Drunken Sailor" is a "stamp-and-go" chantey adapted from a traditional Irish tune. Sailors sang it while hoisting sail, and at the words "Way, hey, and up she rises" the sailors would all stamp on the deck in unison.

With spirit

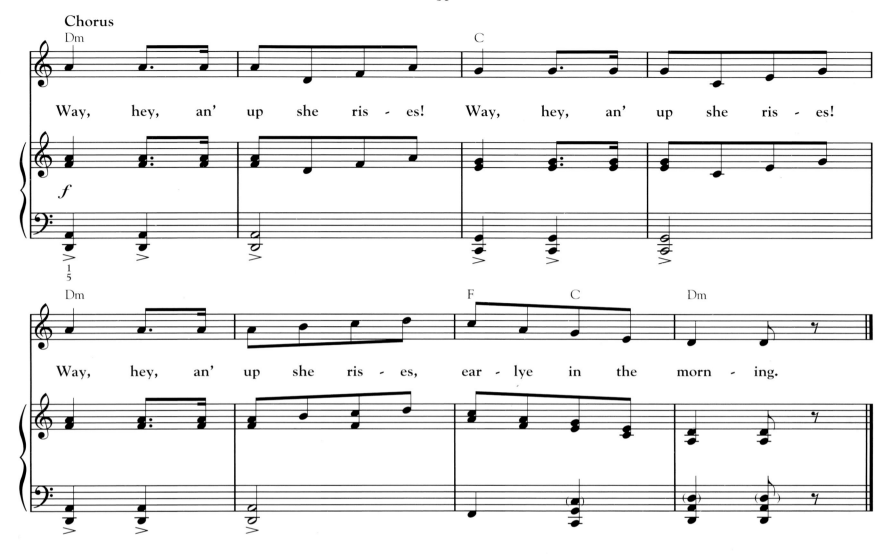

2. Put him in the longboat till he's sober (3x)
   Earlye in the morning.
   (repeat chorus)

3. Put him in a leaky boat and make him bale her (3x)
   Earlye in the morning.
   (repeat chorus)

4. Dip 'im in the drink until he's sober (3x)
   Earlye in the morning.
   (repeat chorus)

The Farmer Is the Man

Traditional

M ANY PEOPLE FORGET THAT THE FARMER who grows the food that we eat is perhaps the most important worker in our society. As this 1870s song reminds us, without farmers we could not live. It was composed at the request of the Midwest Farmer's Alliance to protest the low prices that impoverished many farmers then.

When the farm - er comes to town with his wag - on brok - en down, Oh, the
When the law - yer hangs a - round while the butch - er cuts a pound,

far - mer is the man who feeds them all. _____
If you'll on - ly look and see, I _____
And the preach - er and the cook go a -

think you will a - gree that / the far-mer is the man who feeds them all. ____ The farm-er is the man, the
stroll-ing by the brook. Oh

farm-er is the man, lives on cred-it till the fall. Then they take him by the hand and they
With the int-'rest rate so high, it's a

lead him from the land and the mid-dle-man's the man who gets it all. _____
won - der he don't die, for the mort-gage man's the man who gets it all. _____

Pick A Bale o' Cotton

New words and new music arrangement by Huddie Ledbetter

Collected and adapted by John A. Lomax and Alan Lomax

HUDDIE LEDBETTER (LEADBELLY) sang this dimly remembered slave song in the 1930s and '40s. In truth, no one could pick a bale of cotton in a single day. A bale weighs 500 pounds, and the most that any worker could pick was about 300 pounds. Still, like all the best work songs, this one made the back-breaking labor go a little easier. (For more about Leadbelly, see "In the Pines" on page 72.)

Brightly, like a square dance

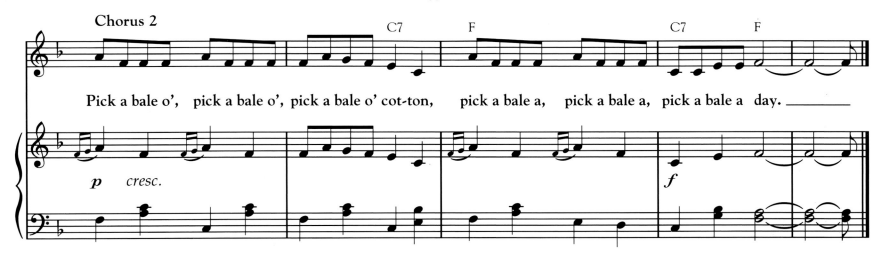

Chorus 2

Pick a bale o', pick a bale o', pick a bale o' cot-ton, pick a bale a, pick a bale a, pick a bale a day. _____

p *cresc.* *f*

3. Had a little woman could pick a bale o' cotton,
Had a little woman could pick a bale a day.
(repeat choruses)

4. (continue similarly)
Me an' my pardner can . . .

5. Looky, looky yonder . . .

Artist unknown
Farm Vignette; United States
Early 20th century
Metal, glass, paint; 65 in.
(165.1 cm) high
Gift of Dorothy and Leo Rabkin
1992.11.1

This Land Is Your Land

Words and Music by Woody Guthrie

Incredibly, this well-known song has never had a hit recording. For years after folk balladeer Woody Guthrie penned it in 1940 it languished in obscurity. Occasionally it was published in collections of school songs, and when the folk revival took hold in the 1950s many young people remembered the song from their school days. This almost guaranteed its popularity, and today it is one of our most beloved songs. Guthrie's colorful life was the subject of a successful movie, *Bound for Glory.* Woody himself died in 1967 of Huntington's chorea, a terrible inherited disease, but his music lives on in spiritual descendants such as Bob Dylan and John Mellencamp, as well as his son, folksinger Arlo Guthrie.

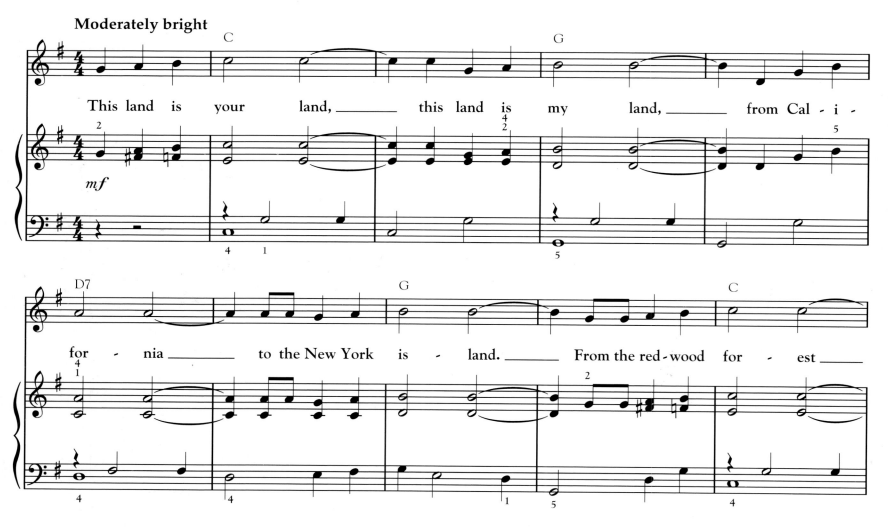

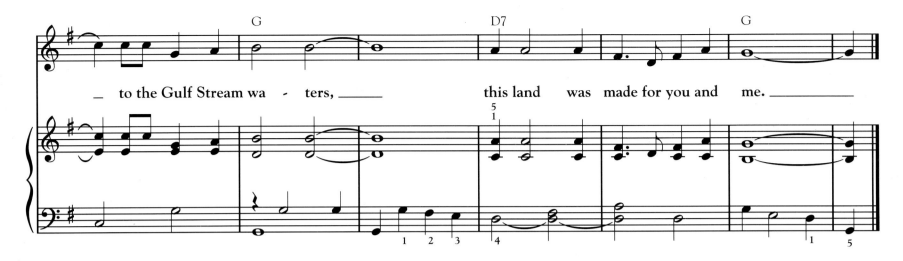

to the Gulf Stream wa - ters, _____ this land was made for you and me. _____

2. As I was walking
   That ribbon of highway,
   I saw above me
   That endless skyway.
   I saw below me
   That golden valley;
   This land was made for you and me.

3. I've roamed and rambled
   And I followed my footsteps
   To the sparkling sands of
   Her diamond deserts,
   And all around me
   A voice was sounding:
   This land was made for you and me.

4. When the sun comes shining
   And I was strolling
   And the wheat fields waving
   And the dust clouds rolling
   As the fog was lifting
   A voice was chanting:
   This land was made for you and me.

Quiltmaker unknown
Map Quilt; Possibly Virginia; dated 1886
Pieced silks, including velvets
and brocades; embroidery
78 3/4 x 82 1/4 in. (200 x 208.9 cm)
Gift of Dr. and Mrs. David C. McLaughlin
1987.1.1

The Water Is Wide

Traditional

THIS BALLAD OF DISAPPOINTED LOVE has graced the world of American folk music since at least the nineteenth century. Its lovely broad melody is based on a Scottish song, "Waly, Waly." Neither the composer of the melody nor the writer of the words is known.

Moderately flowing

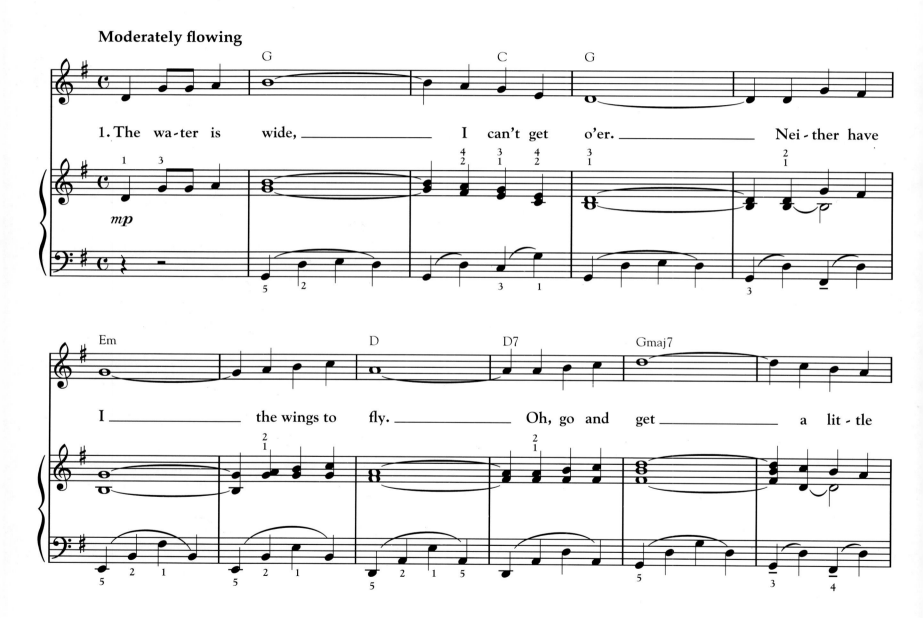

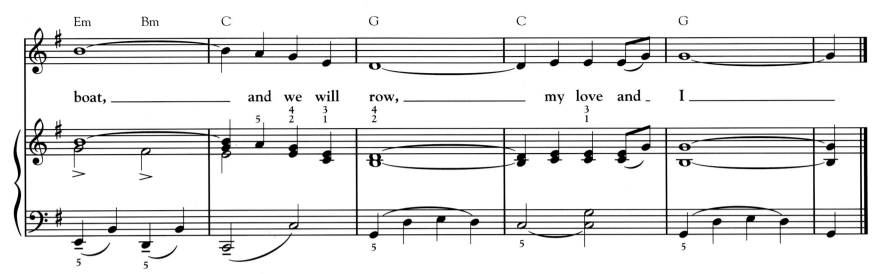

boat, _____ and we will row, _____ my love and _ I _____

2. There is a ship and she sails the sea.
   She's loaded deep, as deep can be,
   But not so deep as the love I'm in.
   I care not if I sink or swim.

3. I lean'd my back against an oak,
   Thinking he was a trusty tree;
   But first he bent, and then he broke,
   And so my love prov'd false to me.

4. I put my hand in a rosy bush,
   Thinking the sweetest flow'r to find.
   I prick'd my finger to the bone,
   And left the sweetest flow'r behind.

5. Oh, love is warm when it is new,
   And love is sweet when it is true;
   But love grows old and waxeth cold,
   And fades away like morning dew.

Attributed to Samuel Folwell (1764–1813)
Woman and Ship; Philadelphia; 1793–1813
Watercolor on ivory, gold bezel, human hair
$2^{1}/_{2}$ x $1^{3}/_{4}$ in. (6.4 x 4.5 cm) oval
Museum of American Folk Art purchase
1981.12.27

Oh! Susanna

Words and Music by Stephen Foster

STEPHEN FOSTER WAS AMERICA'S FIRST PROFESSIONAL songwriter. In his tragically short life he produced some of our most beloved songs, including "Camptown Races," "My Old Kentucky Home," "Beautiful Dreamer," "Old Folks At Home (Way Down Upon the Swanee River)," and this one, written in 1848. The next year gold was discovered in California, and "Oh! Susanna" became the anthem of the Gold Rush of 1849. The song sold many, many copies of sheet music, but Foster had sold all the rights for a few dollars and so never saw further income from it. This lack of business sense plagued him all his life, and he died alone and destitute in 1864 at the age of only thirty-eight.

1. I ___ come from Al - a - bam - a with my ban - jo on my knee, I'm ___
2. I ___ soon will be in New Or - leans and then I'll look a - round, and ___

goin' to Lou - 'si - an - na my _____ true love for to see. It rained all night the
when I find Su - san - na I'll _____ fall up - on the ground. But if I do not

Tom Dooley

Words and music collected, adapted, and arranged by Frank Warner, John A. Lomax, and Alan Lomax

From the singing of Frank Proffitt

THIS MURDER BALLAD is based on the real life of Tom Dula. He had been a loyal soldier for the Confederacy, but after the war he became an outlaw. His pre-war sweetheart, Laura Foster, had waited patiently for him, but her loyalty was betrayed by Tom and his new girlfriend. In 1868 they murdered poor Laura to get her out of the way. Dula tried to escape, but was caught at the Tennessee border and hanged. During the folk revival of the 1950s and '60s the song became an international hit in a version by the Kingston Trio.

there I took her life. Met her on the moun-tain, stabbed her with my knife.

2. This time tomorrow, reckon where I'll be?
Hadn'a been for Grayson, I'd-a been in Tennessee.
(Repeat chorus)

3. This time tomorrow, reckon where I'll be?
Down in some lonesome valley hangin' from a white oak tree.
(Repeat chorus)

Quiltmaker unknown
Bird of Paradise Quilt Top (detail)
Vicinity of Albany, New York; 1858–1863
Appliquéd cotton; wool;
silk including velvet on muslin;
silk embroidery including silk
chenille thread, ink
84¹/₂ x 69⁵/₈ in. (214.6 x 176.9 cm)
Gift of the Trustees of the Museum of
American Folk Art
1979.7.1

On Top of Old Smoky

Traditional

This ballad from the Great Smoky Mountains of North Carolina was first published in 1915. It is similar to "The Wagoner's Lad," an earlier song which told of a girl seduced and then abandoned. (Wagoners were men who moved goods from one part of the country to another. They were similar to the truckers of today.) At that time wagoners had reputations similar to later travelers such as salesmen and sailors. "Old Smoky" still contains this element of true love betrayed, and in this form is a favorite of today's folksingers. A hilarious parody by folksinger Tom Glazer called "On Top of Spaghetti" was a big hit in the 1950s.

Moderately

1. On top of Old Smok — y, all cov-ered with snow, _____ I
lost my true lov - er for a - court-in' too slow. _____

2. Now, courting's a pleasure,
   Parting is grief;
   But a false-hearted lover
   Is worse than a thief.

3. A thief he will rob you
   And take all you have;
   But a false-hearted lover
   Will lead you to the grave.

4. The grave will decay you
   And turn you to dust,
   There ain't one in a million
   A poor girl (boy) can trust.

5. They'll hug you and kiss you
   And tell you more lies
   Than cross ties on the railroad
   Or the stars in the skies.

Karol Kozlowski (1885–1969)
Cabin in the Mountains,
Greenpoint, New York; 1962–1968
Oil on canvas; 29^1/$_2$ x 52 in. (74.9 x 132.1 cm)
The Abril Lamarque Collection. Gift of Lita M. Elvers
1991.21.2

Green Grow the Lilacs

Traditional

THIS SONG WAS WELL KNOWN IN ITS NATIVE IRELAND. It was brought to America by Irish immigrants fleeing the terrible potato famine of 1839–40. Originally the colors referred symbolically to the sacrifice of innocence for love. But when the immigrants got here, they patriotically changed the words to reflect the colors of their new country.

The song became a favorite of American troops during the Mexican War (1846–48). It has been suggested that Mexicans heard the words "green grow" as "gringo," and from there came the derogatory name they gave to all North Americans. *Green Grow the Lilacs* was also the name of a novel by Lynn Riggs, which became the basis for the hit musical *Oklahoma!*

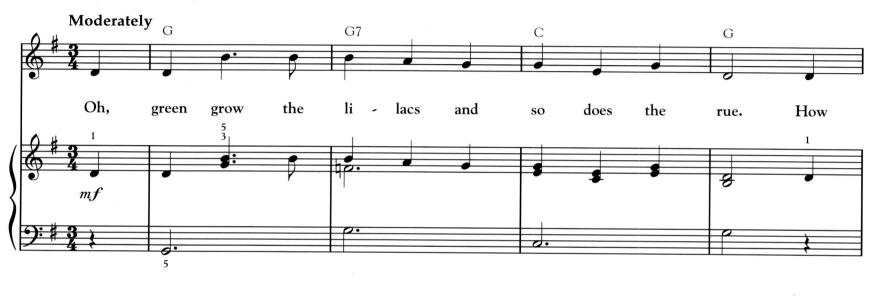

Oh, green grow the li - lacs and so does the rue. How

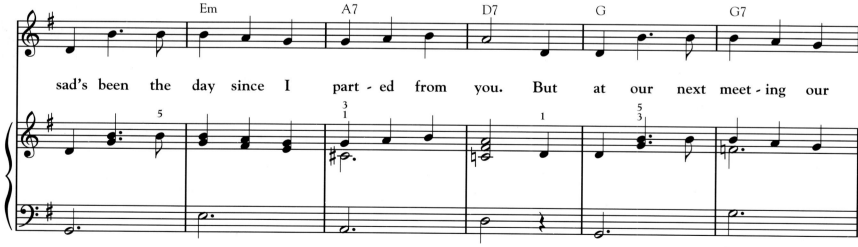

sad's been the day since I part - ed from you. But at our next meet - ing our

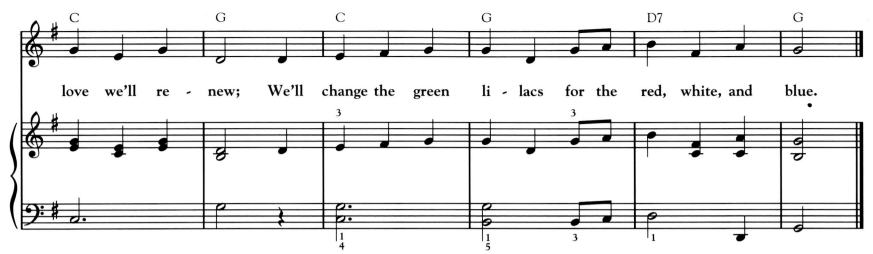

love we'll re - new; We'll change the green li - lacs for the red, white, and blue.

2. I once had a sweetheart but now I have none;
   He's (she's) gone off and left me to live here alone.
   He's (she's) gone off and left me contented to be;
   He (she) must love another better than me.

3. I passed my love's window both early and late;
   The look that he (she) gave me, it made my heart ache.
   The look that he (she) gave me was painful to see,
   For he (she) loves another better than me.

4. I wrote my love letters in red rosy lines,
   He (she) sent me an answer all twisted in twines,
   Saying, "Keep your love letters and I will keep mine;
   Just you write to your love and I'll write to mine."

5. On top of the mountain where green lilacs grow,
   And over the valley where still waters flow
   I met with my love and he (she) proved to be true.
   We changed the green lilacs for the red, white, and blue.

Possibly Gertrude Knappenberger (dates unknown)
Centennial Quilt; possibly Emmaus, Pennsylvania;
dated 1876
Hand-pieced, hand-quilted,
appliquéd, and embroidered cotton
84 x 74 in. (213.4 x 187.9 cm)
Gift of Rhea Goodman
1979.9.1

Nine Hundred Miles

Traditional

THIS HILLBILLY BLUES is one of the best of hundreds that deal with railroads, traveling, and longing for home. Its origins are obscure, but from the modal quality of the melody it is reasonable to suspect an Irish ancestry. Modes are ancient scales which are still found in the folk music of some countries, including Ireland.

Rolling along

1. Well I'm walk-ing down the track, I've got tears in my eyes, try'n to read a let-ter from my home. _____ If that train runs me right I'll be

home to-mor-row night, 'cause I'm nine hun-dred miles from my home, _____ and I

(small notes optional)

hate to hear that lone-some whis-tle blow. _____ (Well, this) blow. _____

2. Well, this train that I ride on
   Is a hundred coaches long;
   You can hear the whistle blow a hundred miles.
   And that lonesome whistle call
   Is the mournfulest of all,
   'Cause it's nine hundred miles from my home,
   And I hate to hear that lonesome whistle blow.

3. Well, I'll pawn for you my watch
   And I'll pawn you my chain,
   Pawn for you my golden diamond ring.
   If that train runs me right
   I'll be home tomorrow night,
   'Cause I'm nine hundred miles from my home,
   And I hate to hear that lonesome whistle blow.

Jack Savitsky (1910–1991)
Train in Coal Town; Lansford, Pennsylvania; c. 1975
Oil on board; 33 x 25 x 1 in. (83.8 x 63.5 x 2.5 cm)
Gift of Mr. and Mrs. Gary J. Stass
1982.15.3

The Bear Went over the Mountain

Traditional

THIS ANCIENT TUNE first became known as "Malbrouk." It recounted the exploits of the Duke of Marlborough, an eighteenth-century British general and ancestor of Britain's courageous World War II leader, Winston Churchill. The tune was well known in France before the Revolution of 1789. In fact, it was sung as a lullaby to Marie Antoinette's children. Later versions called "For He's a Jolly Good Fellow" and "We Won't Go Home Till Morning" appeared in nineteenth century England and America. The first printing of the version called "The Bear Went over the Mountain" appeared in 1919. It must be by an American, because there are no bears in England!

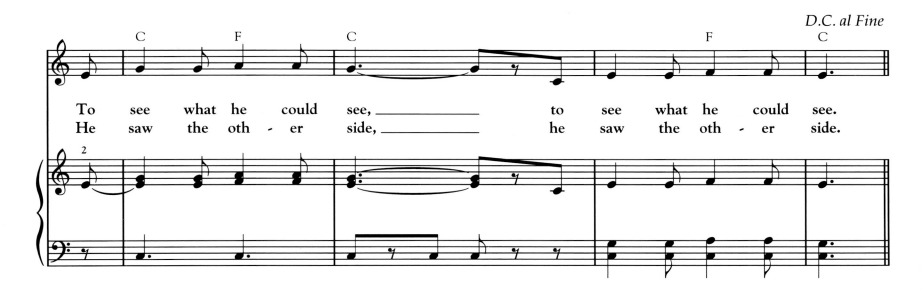

To see what he could see, _____ to see what he could see.
He saw the oth - er side, _____ he saw the oth - er side.

Leroy Archuleta (b. 1949)
Black Bear with Leather Harness
Tesuque, New Mexico; 1988
Painted wood with leather harness, metal toes
59 x 18 x 12 in. (149.9 x 45.7 x 30.5 cm)
Gift of Mrs. Dixon Wecter
1988.16.1

In the Pines

(WHERE DID YOU SLEEP LAST NIGHT?)

New words and new music adaptation by Huddie Ledbetter

KNOWN AS "LEADBELLY," Huddie Ledbetter was one of the most influential folk artists of the twentieth century. Although he was a master of the twelve-string guitar, he was also a fine singer, storyteller, pianist, accordionist, and mandolinist. Unfortunately, he also had a violent temper, and this landed him in prison several times. After he wrote a song in prison begging the governor of Louisiana for a pardon, he was released from the notorious Louisiana State Penitentiary at Angola in 1934. He then had a fairly successful career as a concert performer. Soon after his death from Lou Gehrig's disease in 1949, several of his songs, including "Goodnight, Irene" and "Rock Island Line" became popular hits. More recently, the rock group Nirvana had a hit with "In the Pines," which Leadbelly had adapted from an old Appalachian folk song.

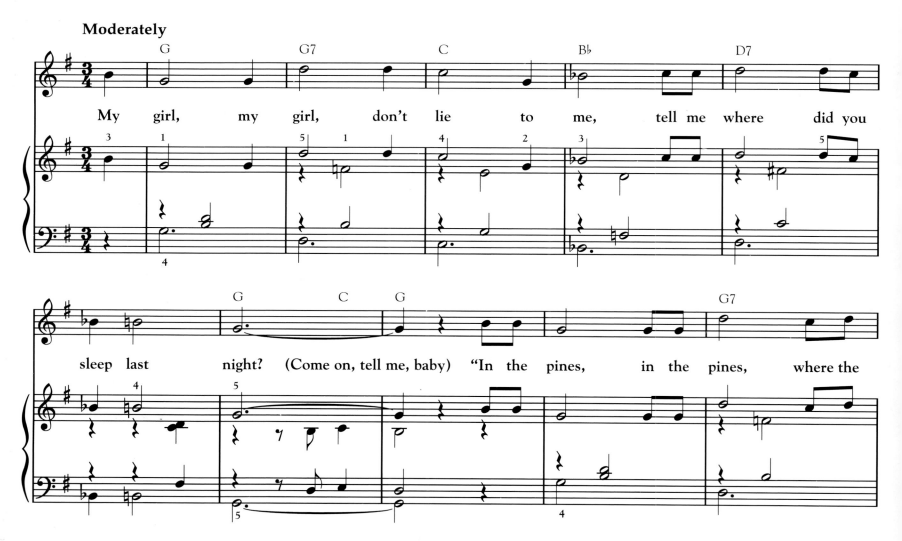

sun don't ev - er shine; I was shiv - rin' the whole night through." _____

2. My girl, my girl, where will you go?
   "I'm goin' where the cold wind blows.
   In the pines, in the pines, where the sun don't ever shine,
   I was shiverin' the whole night through."

3. "My husband was a hard-working man
   Killed a mile and half from here.
   His head was found in a driving wheel
   And his body has never been found."

4. (repeat first verse)

Sarah Ann Garges (c. 1834–1887)
Sarah Ann Garges Quilt
Doylestown, Pennsylvania; dated 1853
Hand-sewn, pieced, and appliquéd
cotton, silk, wool, and wool embroidery
96 x 98 in. (243.8 x 248.9 cm.)
Gift of Warner Communications, Inc.
1988.21.1

Down in the Valley

Traditional

FIRST PRINTED IN 1917, this simple and lovely folk melody has had many different lyrics. A common thread is the nostalgia felt by mountain boys who were forced to live, or be imprisoned in, the lowlands. The song has also been known as "Bird in a Cage," "Down on the Levee," and "Birmingham Jail."

This is the best-known version about love and loneliness. Because the accompaniment can be played using only two chords, it is a favorite of beginning folk guitarists and banjo players.

1. Down in the val - ley, val - ley so low; _____
   Hear the wind blow, love, hear the wind blow; _____

Hang your head o - ver, hear the wind blow. _____
Hang your head o - ver, hear the wind blow. _____

Play after last verse only

2. If you don't love me, then love who you please,
   Throw your arms 'round me, give my heart ease.
   Give my heart ease, love, give my heart ease,
   Throw your arms 'round me, give my heart ease.

3. Roses love sunshine, violets love dew;
   Angels in heaven know I love you.
   Know I love you, dear, know I love you,
   Angels in heaven know I love you.

Paul A. Seifert (1840–1921)
The Residence of Lemuel Cooper
Plain, Wisconsin; 1879
Watercolor, oil, and tempera on paper
21 7/8 x 28 in. (55.6 x 71.1 cm)
Museum of American Folk Art purchase
1981.12.26

Frankie and Johnny

Traditional

MANY VERSIONS OF THIS BLUES SONG were published in the early 1900s. The song is also known as "Frankie and Albert" and is thought to refer to a real couple, Albert Britt and Frances (Frankie) Baker. Britt was a St. Louis lowlife who was shot to death by girlfriend Frankie in 1899.

1. Frank-ie and John-ny were sweet-hearts, __ oh, Lord-y, how they could love. They swore to be true to each oth-er, __ true as the stars a-bove. He was her man,

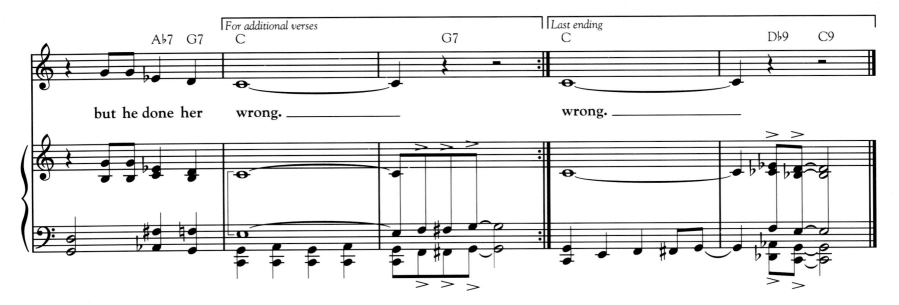

2. Frankie went down to the corner, just for a bucket of beer,
   She said to the fat bartender, "Has my lovin' man been here?"
   He was her man, but he done her wrong.

3. "I don't want to cause you no trouble, I don't want to tell you no lie,
   But I saw your man 'bout an hour ago with a gal named Nellie Bly.
   If he's your man, he's a doin' you wrong."

4. Frankie looked over the transom and found to her great surprise
   That there on the bed sat Johnny, makin' love to Nellie Bly.
   He was her man, but he done her wrong.

5. Frankie drew back her kimono, she took out her big forty-four.
   Rooty-toot-toot, that gal did shoot right through that hardwood door.
   He was her man, but he done her wrong.

6. "Roll me over real easy. Roll me over real slow.
   Roll me on my right side 'cause the bullet hurts me so.
   I was your man, but I was doin' you wrong."

7. Frankie went to his coffin, she looked down on his face.
   Said, "Lord, have mercy on me, I wish I could take his place.
   He was my man, but I done him wrong!"

Casey Jones

(THE BRAVE ENGINEER)

Words by T. Lawrence Seibert

Music by Eddie Newton

THIS 1909 BALLAD TELLS THE STORY of a real 1906 train wreck and a heroic engineer, John Luther Jones. Nicknamed "Casey" for his hometown of Cayce, Kentucky, Jones was the engineer on a southbound mail train running from Memphis, Tennessee, to Canton, Mississippi. Trying to make up lost time, Casey was "highballing" at over sixty miles per hour. But when he came around a curve he saw to his horror that a freight train was partially blocking the main line. Commanding his fireman to jump, Casey died at the throttle vainly trying to minimize the inevitable collision. Many songs were written about the heroic engineer, but this is the one that has survived.

1. Come, all you round-ers, if you want to hear a sto-ry 'bout a

brave en-gi-neer. Ca-sey Jones was the round-er's name, on a

2. "Put in your water and shovel your coal;
   Put your head out the window, watch them drivers roll!
   I'll run her till she leaves the rail
   'Cause I'm eight hours late with that western mail."
   He looked at his watch, and his watch was slow;
   He looked at the water and the water was low.
   He turned to the fireman and then he said:
   "We're goin' to reach Frisco, but we'll all be dead!"
   Casey Jones, goin' to reach Frisco,
   Casey Jones, but we'll all be dead.
   Casey Jones, goin' to reach Frisco;
   We're goin' to reach Frisco, but we'll all be dead!

3. Casey pulled up that Reno hill;
   He tooted for the crossing with an awful shrill.
   The switchman knew by the engine's moan
   That the man at the throttle was Casey Jones.
   He pulled up within two miles of the place;
   Number Four stared him right in the face.
   He turned to the fireman, said, "Boy, you better jump,
   'Cause there's two locomotives that's a-goin' to bump."
   Casey Jones, two locomotives,
   Casey Jones, that's a-goin' to bump.
   Casey Jones, two locomotives,
   There's two locomotives that's a-goin' to bump.

4. Casey said, just before he died,
   "There's two more roads that I'd like to ride."
   The fireman said, "What could they be?"
   "The Southern Pacific and the Santa Fe."
   Mrs. Jones sat on her bed a-sighin'
   Just received a message that Casey was dyin'.
   Said, "Go to bed, children, and hush your cryin'
   'Cause you got another papa on the Salt Lake Line."
   Mrs. Casey Jones, got another papa,
   Mrs. Casey Jones, on the Salt Lake Line.
   Mrs. Casey Jones, got another papa,
   And you've got another papa on the Salt Lake Line.

Weaver unknown
Fancy-weave Doublecloth Coverlet:
Snowflake Medallion with Hemfield Railroad Border
Pennsylvania; c. 1850–1857
Wool and cotton; $90^{1}/_{4}$ x 81 in.
Gift of Stephen L. Snow
1980.13.1

Joshua Fit the Battle of Jericho

Traditional

LIKE MANY AFRICAN-AMERICAN SPIRITUALS, "Joshua" became known after the Civil War. The black slaves identified with the plight of the Israelites held captive in Egypt and saw the fall of the walls of Jericho as the fall of the institution of slavery itself. "Fit" is a dialect pronunciation of "fought."

Moderately fast, with a solid beat

2. Well, the Lord done told old Joshua:
   "You must do just what I say,
   March around that city seven times
   And the walls will tumble away."

3. So up to the walls of Jericho,
   He marched with spear in hand,
   "Go blow them ram horns," Joshua cried,
   "'Cause the battle am in my hand."

Go Down, Moses

Traditional

AFRICAN-AMERICAN MUSIC had been virtually ignored by white society before the Civil War. But it started coming into its own in the latter part of the nineteenth century. This moving spiritual tells the story of the Israelites' captivity in ancient Egypt and their longing to be free. The slaves in America identified with this story and had similar yearnings. Some writers suggest that the song is about Harriet Tubman (nicknamed "Moses"), the great African-American leader whose efforts saved thousands of runaway black slaves on the "Underground Railroad."

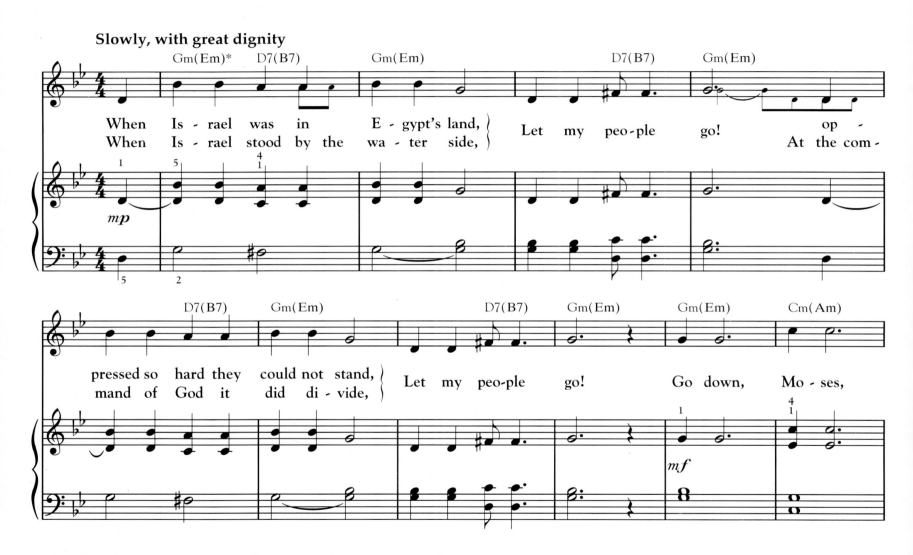

*Chord symbols in parentheses are for guitar with capo across 3rd fret.

way down in E - gypt's land. Tell - ol' Pha - raoh: Let my peo-ple go!

Quiltmaker unknown
Bird of Paradise Quilt Top (detail)
Vicinity of Albany, New York; 1858–1863
Appliquéd cotton; wool; silk including velvet on muslin;
silk embroidery including silk chenille thread, ink
$84^1/_2$ x $69^5/_8$ in. (214.6 x 176.9 cm)
Gift of the Trustees of the Museum of American Folk Art
1979.7.1

When Jesus Wept

By William Billings

Harmonized by D.F.

WILLIAM BILLINGS WAS A TRUE AMERICAN ORIGINAL. Blind in one eye, short of leg, raucous of voice, and uncouth of manner, he wrote what he called "fuguing tunes," contrapuntal hymns of startling originality. He was dismissed as a semiliterate eccentric by his contemporaries, but his music was rediscovered by Aaron Copeland and other modern American composers who recognized its true beauty and originality. This hymn can also be sung as a round. The second voice enters at 1 when the first voice gets to 2. The third voice enters at 1 when the second voice gets to 2 and so on.

trem - bling fear seized all _____ the guilt - y world ___ a - round.

Nan Phelps (1904–1990)
Crucifixion; Hamilton, Ohio; 1940
Oil on canvas; 55 1/4 x 34 in.
(140.3 x 86.4 cm.)
Gift of Robert Phelps in loving memory
of his wife, Nan Phelps
1992.18.2

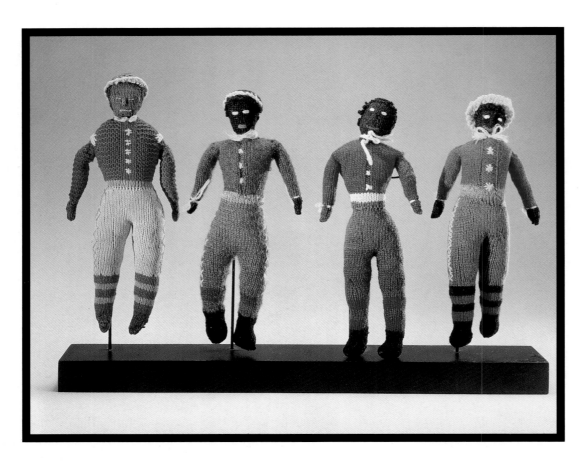

Artist unknown
Four Hand-knitted and Stuffed Dolls
Possibly Maine; 1870–1880
Wool yarn with embroidered features,
stuffed with cotton and straw or sawdust
11^1/$_2$ x 5^1/$_2$ x 1^1/$_4$ in. (29.2 x 13.9 x 3.2 cm)
Gift of Robert Bishop
1986.3.4a–d

Rock-a-My Soul

Traditional

THIS AFRICAN-AMERICAN SPIRITUAL had been all but forgotten when the white folk group Peter, Paul, and Mary recorded it in the early 1960s. Its theme of overcoming adversity by hard work and determination is as appropriate today as when it was first sung by slaves and then by black gospel groups beginning around the time of the Civil War.

With a solid beat

1. Oh, rock-a-my soul in the bos - som of A - bra-ham, rock-a-my soul in the bos - om of A - bra-ham, rock-a-my soul in the bos - om of A - bra-ham, Oh, rock-a-my soul.

2. So high you can't get o - ver it, so low you can't get un - der it, so wide you can't get 'round it; you must go in at the door.

When the Saints Go Marching In

Traditional

"THE SAINTS" STARTED OUT AS "The Old Ship of Zion," a white campmeeting song. Blacks borrowed it and gave it the words we sing today. First published in 1896, the song was played by New Orleans jazz bands at funerals. On the way *to* the cemetery it was played slowly and mournfully. On the way back *from* the cemetery the tempo was sped up, and the song began to sound like the Dixieland jazz favorite of today. Nowadays it is the most requested Dixieland jazz tune.

With a solid beat

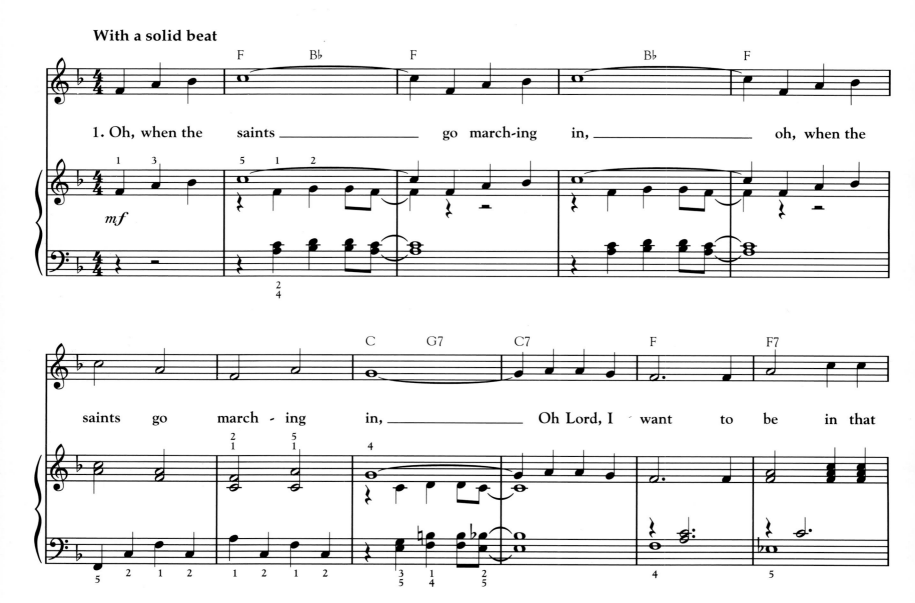

1. Oh, when the saints _____ go march-ing in, _____ oh, when the

saints go march - ing in, _____ Oh Lord, I want to be in that

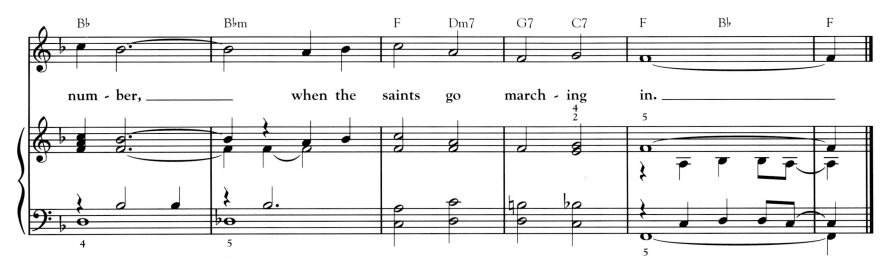

num - ber, _____ when the saints go march - ing in. _____

2. And when that sun begins to shine,
   And when that sun begins to shine,
   Oh Lord, I want to be in that number,
   When the sun begins to shine.

3. And when the revelation comes,
   And when that revelation comes,
   Oh Lord, I want to be in that number,
   When the revelation comes.

4. And when the saints go marching in,
   And when the saints go marching in,
   Oh Lord, I want to be in that number,
   When the saints go marching in.

Sister Gertrude Morgan (1900–1980)
New Jerusalem; New Orleans, Louisiana; c. 1970
Acrylic and tempera on cardboard
12 x 19 in. (30.5 x 48.3 cm)
Gift of Sanford and Patricia Smith
1986.21.1

Old Time Religion

Traditional

THIS HAND-CLAPPING SPIRITUAL is an all-time favorite in both white and black churches. Its origins are obscure. We do know that it first appeared in print shortly after the Civil War. It's a wonderful tune to clap your hands on. In black churches they clap on the second and fourth beats of each measure. In white churches they clap on the first and third beats.

Bright and spirited

Chorus

Gim-me that old time re - li - gion, gim-me that old time re - li - gion, gim-me that old time re - li - gion; it's good e - nough for me.

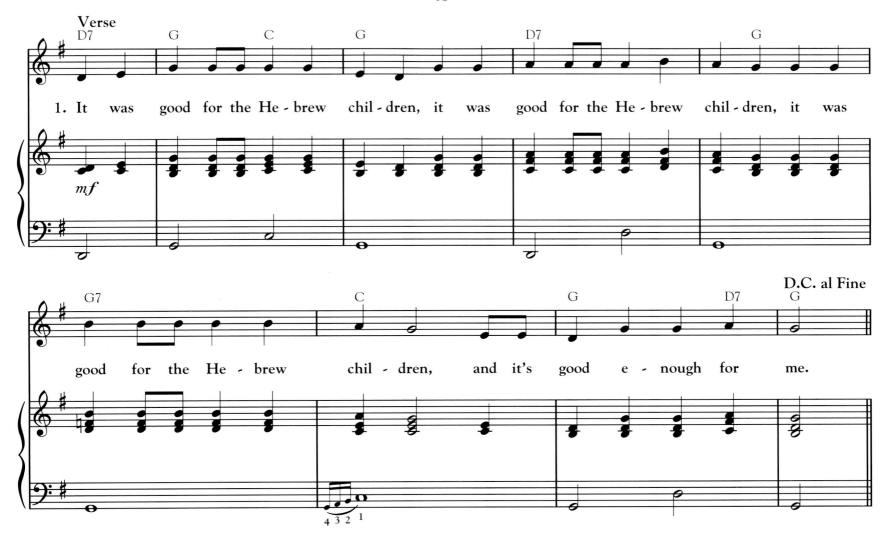

Verse

1. It was good for the He-brew chil-dren, it was good for the He-brew chil-dren, it was good for the He-brew chil-dren, and it's good e-nough for me.

D.C. al Fine

2. It was good for Paul and Silas,
It was good for Paul and Silas,
It was good for Paul and Silas,
And it's good enough for me.
(repeat chorus)

3. (continue similarly)
It was good enough for father . . .

4. It was good for my grandpappy . . .

5. It was good for dear old mammy . . .

6. (repeat first verse and chorus)

Emily Lunde (b. 1914)
Cottage Meeting, 1914; North Dakota; 1976
Oil on board; 18 x 24 in. (45.7 x 60.9 cm)
Gift of the artist
1978.3.1

Down by the Riverside

Traditional

THIS AFRICAN-AMERICAN SPIRITUAL dates back to the time of the Civil War. Its words, which reject the whole idea of war, may have even been inspired by the terrible bloodshed in that epic struggle. The song lives on today mostly through the efforts of Dixieland jazz musicians, with whom it is a great favorite.

Moderately fast, with a swinging beat

1. Gon-na lay down my sword and shield __ down by the riv-er-side, __ down by the riv-er-side, __ down by the riv-er-side. __ Gon-na lay down my sword and shield __

down by the riv - er - side, __ down by the riv - er - side. _____ I ain't gon-na

Chorus

stud-y war no more, I ain't gon-na stud-y war no more, I ain't gon-na stud - y _____

war no more. _____ I ain't gon-na more. _____

2. Gonna meet my Lord Jesus, down by the riverside . . .
3. Gonna put on my long white robe . . .
4. Gonna meet with my brothers . . .
5. Gonna meet with my sisters . . .
6. Gonna lay down my sword and shield . . .

All My Trials

Traditional

THIS BAPTIST HYMN became known in the South some time after the Civil War (1861–65). It then found its way to the Bahamas, where it picked up its unusual modal flavor. This use of ancient modal scales and the unique rhythmical feeling and plaintive words made it a favorite of the folk music revival in the 1950s and '60s. Folksinger Odetta's heart-wrenching recording is especially notable from that time.

2. Now, hush little baby, don't you cry,
   You know that man is born to die.
   (repeat chorus)

3. I had a little book that was given to me,
   And ev'ry page spelled victory.
   (repeat chorus)

Amazing Grace

Words by John Newton   *Music: Traditional*

JOHN NEWTON WAS THE CAPTAIN of a ship that brought African slaves to the American colonies in the early eighteenth century. After a terrible storm almost sank his ship, Newton became convinced that God was telling him the slave trade was evil. Newton gave up slaving and became a preacher and writer of the lyrics for many hymns, of which this is his most famous. The composer of the music is unknown, but a recent recording featuring a bagpipe band sounds so natural that it's reasonable to think that the tune is of Scottish origin.

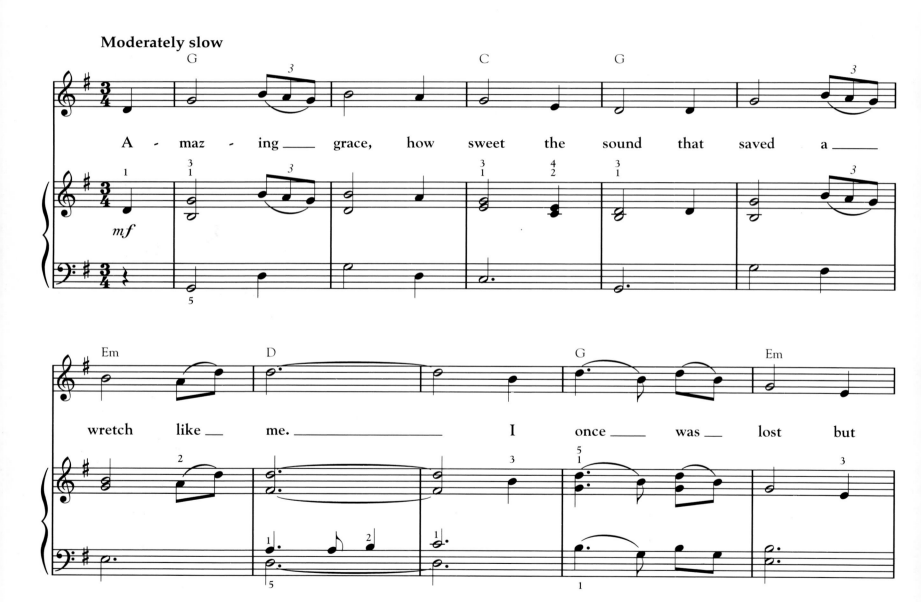

Moderately slow

A - maz - ing ___ grace, how sweet the sound that saved a ___

wretch like ___ me. ___ I once ___ was ___ lost but

now ___ am ___ found, was blind, but ___ now I see. _____

2. 'Twas grace that taught my heart to fear,
   And grace my fears relieved;
   How precious did that grace appear
   The hour I first believed!

3. Through many dangers, toils, and snares,
   I have already come;
   'Tis grace has brought me safe thus far,
   And grace will lead me home.

4. The Lord has promised good to me,
   His word my hope secures;
   He will my shield and portion be
   As long as life endures.

5. The earth shall soon dissolve like snow;
   The sun forbear to shine;
   But God, who called me here below,
   Will be forever mine.

Lorenzo Scott (b. 1934)
Jesus Rose Lazarus from the Dead
Atlanta, Georgia; c. 1982
Oil on particle board, gilded yellow pine with automobile repair material
52 x 43 in. (132.1 x 109.2 cm)
Gift of W. Marvin Clary, William H. Clary, Jane E. Hunecke, and Albert L. Hunecke, Jr.
1991.35.1

Kum Ba Ya

Traditional

KUM (PRONOUNCED KOOM) BA YA is the way Africans pronounced "Come by here," when they heard it from missionaries in the early nineteenth century. Later, the spiritual found its way to the United States, where it became a great favorite of blacks and whites. The unusual meter is played like one measure of 4/4 time followed by one measure of 2/4.

2. Someone's praying, Lord, Kum ba ya,
Someone's praying, Lord, Kum ba ya,
Someone's praying, Lord, Kum ba ya,
Oh Lord, Kum ba ya.

3. (continue similarly)
Someone's singing, Lord, . . .

4. Someone's weeping, Lord, . . .

Clementine Hunter (1886/87–1988)
Black Christ on Cross; Melrose Plantation,
Natchitoches, Louisiana; c. 1972
Oil on canvas,
26¹/₂ x 11¹/₂ in. (66.5 x 29.3 cm)
Gift of Mrs. Chauncey Newlin
1991.23.1

Buffalo Gals

Traditional

IN THE EARLY DAYS OF MINSTRELSY, about 1830, a performer named John Hodges called himself "Cool White." He penned a catchy ditty he called (in sort of a mock-Negro dialect) "Lubly (that is, 'lovely') Fan, Won'tcha Come Out Tonight?" Later performers, traveling from city to city, inserted local names into the song. In various cities the song became "New York Gals Won'tcha Come Out

Tonight?" "Cleveland Gals . . ." and so on. For some reason "Buffalo Gals" became the best known, and that's how the song is known today. In the 1940s, the singing Andrews Sisters recorded an updated version of "Buffalo Gals" called "Dance With a Dolly (With a Hole in Her Stocking)" that became a big hit and reintroduced the song to America.

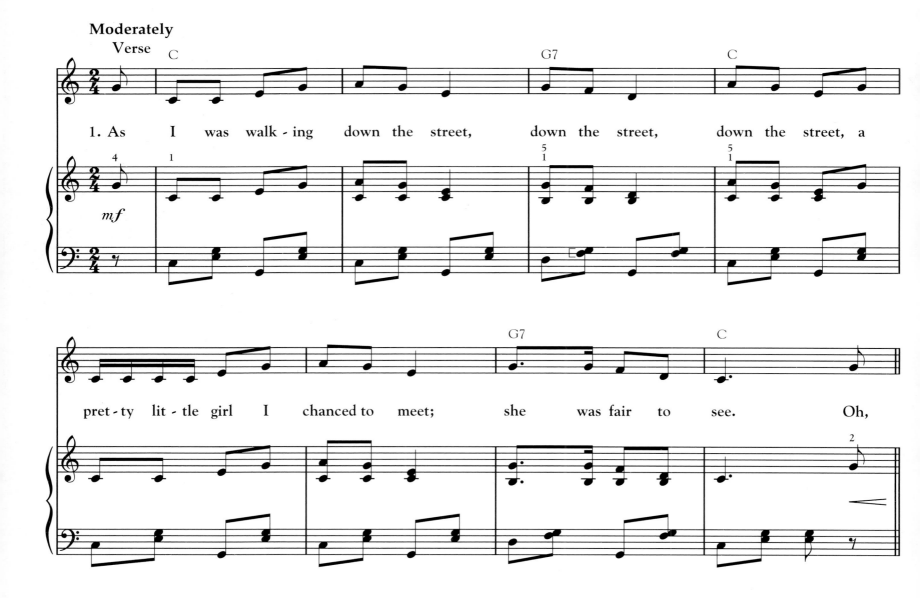

Chorus

Buf-fa-lo gals, won't-cha come out to-night, come out to-night, come out to-night? Oh,

Buf-fa-lo gals, won't-cha come out to-night and dance by the light of the moon? _____

2. I asked her if she'd like some talk,
   Like some talk, stop and talk.
   Her feet took up the whole sidewalk,
   She was fair to see.
   (repeat chorus)

3. I asked her if she'd be my wife,
   Be my wife, be my wife.
   Then I'd be happy all my life
   If she'd marry me.
   (repeat chorus)

Turkey in the Straw

Traditional

ONE DAY IN THE EARLY 1820s, an entertainer named Daddy Rice saw an old black man singing a ditty and doing a peculiar hopping dance on the street. Rice was fascinated. He studied the dance and the next week did his own version, which he called "Jump Jim Crow." For music he used a half-remembered Irish reel called "Old Zip Coon," and soon it seemed as though everyone was singing it.

About forty years later entertainer Dan Bryant of the famous "Bryant's Minstrels" wrote a new set of words to "Old Zip Coon," the ones we sing today as "Turkey in the Straw." But the expression Jim Crow did not die out. Instead, it became the name of the shameful practice of segregating blacks from whites.

1. As __ I was go - in' down the road with a tired __ team and a heav-y load, I ___ crack my whip and the lead-er sprung. I says day-day to the wag-on tongue.

Chorus

Tur-key in the straw, tur-key in the hay, tur-key in the straw, tur-key in the hay,

Roll-'em up, twist-'em up, high tuck-a-haw and _ play 'em up a tune_called "Tur-key in the Straw."

2. I came to a river and I couldn't get across,
   I paid five dollars for a blind old hoss;
   Wouldn't go ahead and he wouldn't stand still,
   So he went up and down like an old saw mill.
   (Repeat chorus)

3. As I came down the new log road,
   Met Mr. Bullfrog, met Miss Toad,
   And every time Miss Toad would sing,
   Ole Bullfrog cut a pigeon wing.
   (Repeat chorus)

4. Went out to milk but I didn't know how,
   I milked the goat instead of the cow.
   A monkey was sittin' on a pile of straw,
   A-winkin' at my mother-in-law.
   (Repeat chorus)

Quiltmaker unknown
Bird of Paradise Quilt Top (detail)
Vicinity of Albany, New York; 1858–1863
Appliquéd cotton; wool;
silk including velvet on muslin;
silk embroidery including silk
chenille thread, ink
$84^1/_2$ x $69^5/_8$ in. (214.6 x 176.9 cm)
Gift of the Trustees of the Museum of
American Folk Art
1979.7.1

M-O-T-H-E-R

(A Word That Means the World to Me)

Words by Howard Johnson

Music by Theodore Morse

THE PERIOD BEFORE WORLD WAR I was one of great sentimentality in Tin Pan Alley, the name given to 28th Street in New York City, where most song publishers had their offices. Many a song told of love—lost, found, unrequited, true, false, and remembered from long ago. Mother love was also a favorite theme. Unlike today when mothers are often blamed for their childrens' ills, mothers of long ago were idealized and painted in the most glowing colors. This song can still bring a tear to the eyes of the most hard-hearted audience.

Wait Till the Sun Shines, Nellie

Words by Andrew B. Sterling

Music by Harry von Tilzer

WALKING DOWN THE STREET ONE DAY, professional tunesmith Harry von Tilzer witnessed a family being evicted from their apartment. He overheard a friend comforting the family with the words: "The sun will shine after the storm." Pausing for a moment to donate a few dollars to the unfortunate family, von Tilzer rushed back to his office in Tin Pan Alley and, with partner Andrew Sterling, turned out this inspirational classic. The song title was also used in a 1952 movie that chronicled the triumphs and tragedies of a small-town barber.

My Wild Irish Rose

Words and Music by Chauncey Olcott

Nᴏᴛ ᴀ ꜱᴏɴɢ ꜰʀᴏᴍ Iʀᴇʟᴀɴᴅ, this ballad was written for the American show *A Romance of Athlone* (1899) by Irish-American Chauncey Olcott. It was one of the earliest that began the ongoing love affair Americans have with the Irish and their music. *My Wild Irish Rose* was also the title of Olcott's screen biography (1947) starring Dennis Morgan. The movie featured many of Olcott's other hits too, including "When Irish Eyes Are Smiling," which is probably the best known of all Irish-American songs.

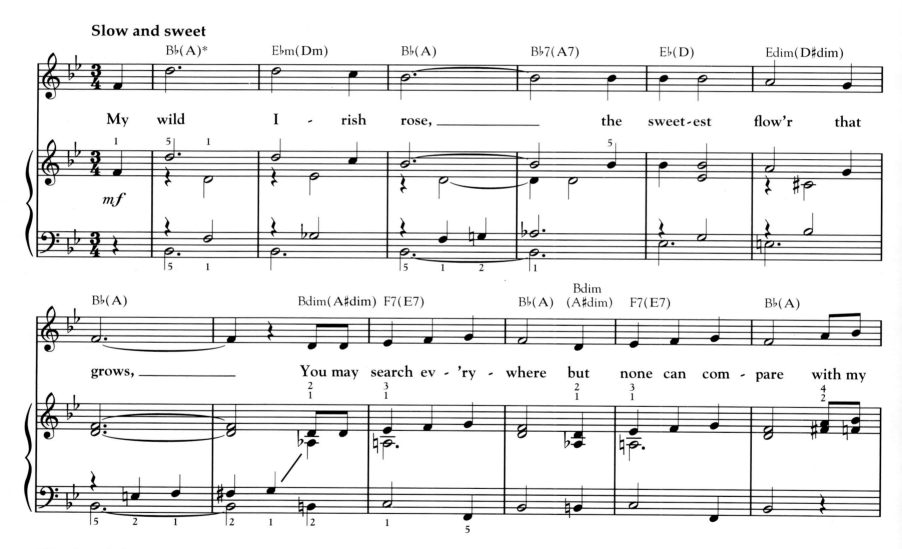

*Chord symbols in parentheses are for guitar with capo across 1st fret.

Index

Quiltmaker unknown
Bird of Paradise Quilt Top (detail)
Vicinity of Albany, New York; 1858–1863
Appliquéd cotton; wool;
silk including velvet on muslin;
silk embroidery including silk
chenille thread, ink
$84^1/_2$ x $69^5/_8$ in. (214.6 x 176.9 cm)
Gift of the Trustees of the Museum of
American Folk Art
1979.7.1

Artist unknown
Friendship Pin (Clasped Hands)
United States; c. 1830
Watercolor on ivory
$7/_8$ x $1^1/_8$ in. (2.2 x 2.9 cm.)
Joseph Martinson Memorial Fund,
Frances and Paul Martinson
1981.12.31

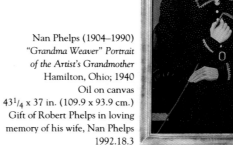

Nan Phelps (1904–1990)
*"Grandma Weaver" Portrait
of the Artist's Grandmother*
Hamilton, Ohio; 1940
Oil on canvas
$43^1/_4$ x 37 in. (109.9 x 93.9 cm.)
Gift of Robert Phelps in loving
memory of his wife, Nan Phelps
1992.18.3